A SELECTION OF FIFTY-FIVE SONGS FROM

THE WORLD'S GREATEST

ARTISTS AND BANDS • CHORD SONGBOOK

PUBLISHED BY
WISE PUBLICATIONS,
8/9 FRITH STREET, LONDON
W1D 3JB, ENGLAND.

EXCLUSIVE DISTRIBUTORS:

MUSIC SALES LIMITED,
DISTRIBUTION CENTRE, NEWMARKET ROAD,
BURY ST EDMUNDS, SUFFOLK,
IP33 3YB, ENGLAND.

MUSIC SALES PTY LIMITED,
120 ROTHSCHILD AVENUE, ROSEBERY,
NSW 2018, AUSTRALIA.

ORDER NO. AM91967
ISBN 0-7119-4083-5

MUSIC ARRANGED BY MATT PARSONS.
ENGRAVED BY PAUL EWERS MUSIC DESIGN.

PRINTED IN GREAT BRITAIN.

WISE PUBLICATIONS
PART OF THE MUSIC SALES GROUP
LONDON/NEW YORK/PARIS/SYDNEY/COPENHAGEN/BERLIN/MADRID/TOKYO

Killer Queen

Words & Music by
Freddie Mercury

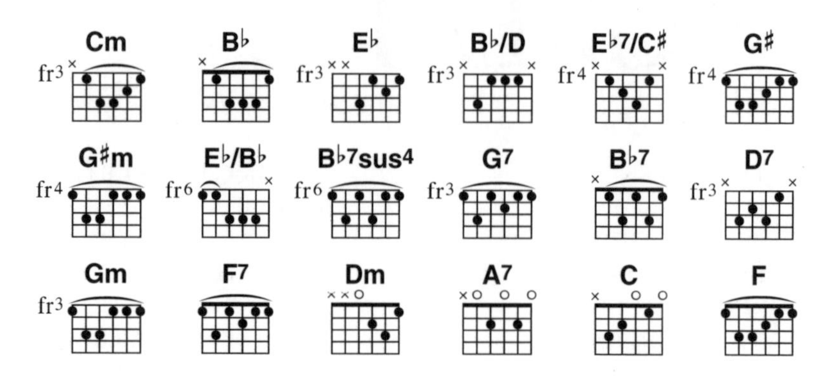

Verse 1

Cm
She keeps Moet et Chandon
B♭
In her pretty cabinet
Cm
"Let them eat cake" she says
B♭
Just like Marie Antoinette
E♭ B♭/D
A built-in remedy
E♭7/C♯ G♯
For Kruschev and Kennedy
G♯m E♭/B♭
At anytime an invitation
B♭7sus4
You can't de - cline.
G7 Cm
Caviar and cigarettes
B♭7 E♭
Well versed in etiquette
D7 Gm
Extra - ordinarily nice.

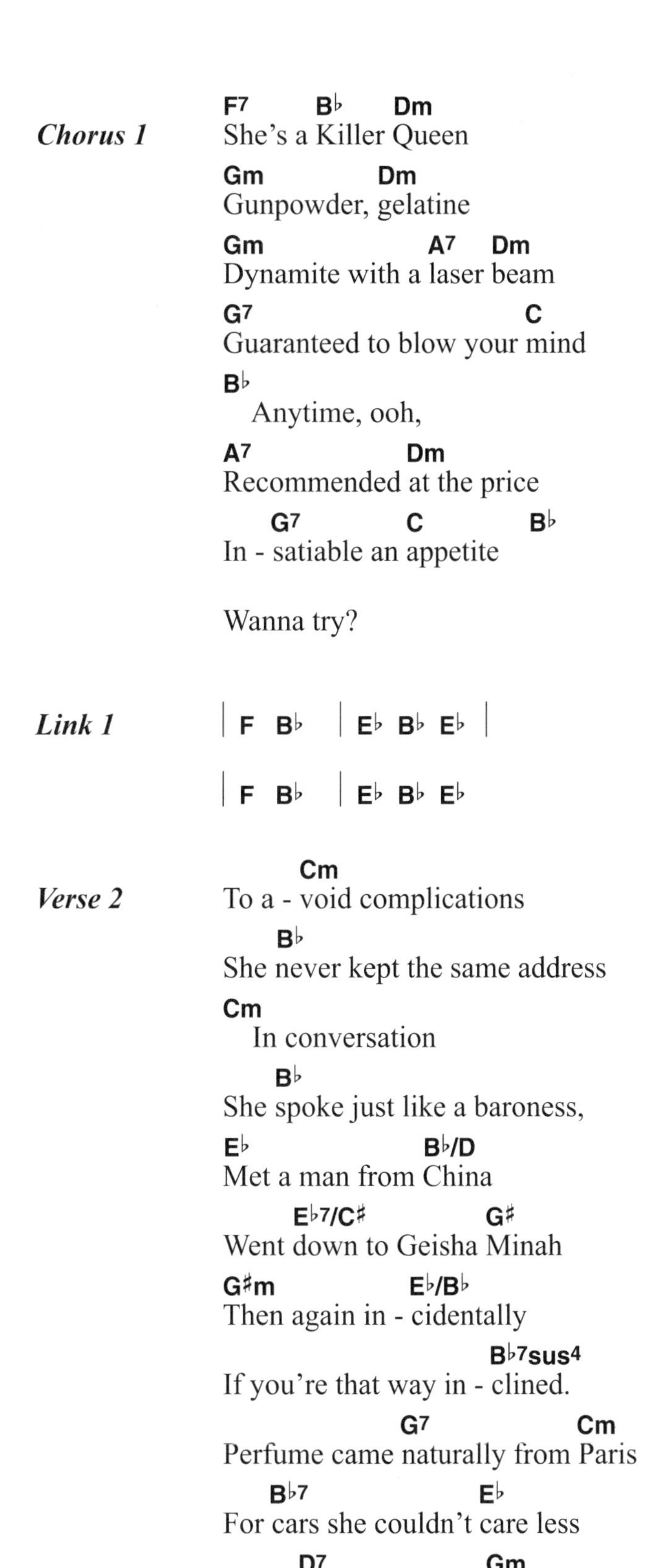

Chorus 1

F7 B♭ Dm
She's a Killer Queen
Gm Dm
Gunpowder, gelatine
Gm A7 Dm
Dynamite with a laser beam
G7 C
Guaranteed to blow your mind
B♭
Anytime, ooh,
A7 Dm
Recommended at the price
G7 C B♭
In - satiable an appetite

Wanna try?

Link 1

| F B♭ | E♭ B♭ E♭ |

| F B♭ | E♭ B♭ E♭

Verse 2

Cm
To a - void complications
B♭
She never kept the same address
Cm
In conversation
B♭
She spoke just like a baroness,
E♭ B♭/D
Met a man from China
E♭7/C♯ G♯
Went down to Geisha Minah
G♯m E♭/B♭
Then again in - cidentally
B♭7sus4
If you're that way in - clined.
G7 Cm
Perfume came naturally from Paris
B♭7 E♭
For cars she couldn't care less
D7 Gm
Fast - idious and pre - cise.

Chorus 2

```
F7       B♭     Dm
She's a Killer Queen
Gm            Dm
Gunpowder, gelatine
Gm                  A7   Dm
Dynamite with a laser beam
G7                            C
Guaranteed to blow your mind
B♭
   Anytime.
```

Guitar Solo

```
| A7  Dm | A7  Dm | G7  Cm | G7 C  F |
| F      | F      | F (fermata) |
| Cm     | B♭     | Cm     |
| B♭     | E♭ B♭/D | E♭7   | C#     | G#     |
| G#m E♭/B♭ | B♭7sus4 ||
```

Verse 3

```
N.C.      G7            Cm
Drop of a hat she's as willing as
G7          Cm
Playful as a pussy cat
     B♭              E♭
Then momentarily out of action
B♭            E♭
Temporarily out of gas
   D7           Gm   F    B♭    F B♭m
To absolutely drive you wild,—wild
            F
She's all out to get you.
```

Chorus 3

```
F7        B♭      Dm
She's a Killer Queen
Gm              Dm
Gunpowder, gelatine
Gm                   A7     Dm
Dynamite with a laser beam
G7                               C
Guaranteed to blow your mind
B♭
   Anytime.
A7                  Dm
Recommended at the price
     G7            C             B♭
In - satiable an appetite

Wanna try?
```

Outro

| F B♭ | E♭ F | B♭ E♭ |

| F B♭ | E♭ F | B♭ E♭ |: E♭ :| *To fade*

Heroes

Words & Music by
David Bowie

D G C Am Em

```
Intro     |: D     | D     | G     | G     :|

          D              G        D                   G
Verse 1   I, I will be king, and you, you will be queen.
                       C                          D
          Though nothing, will drive them away
                   Am          Em              D
          We can beat them,     just for one day.
                       C        G             D
          We can be heroes,  just for one day.
                                       G
          And you, you can be mean.
              D                    G
          And I, I'll drink all the time
                          D                      G
          'Cause we're lovers, and that is a fact.
                          D                      G
          Yes we're lovers, and that is that.
                       C                        D
          Though nothing, will keep us together
                                  Am      Em            D
          We could steal time,        just for one day.
                          C       G                      D
          We can be heroes,       for ever and ever.  What d'you say?

Link 1    |: D     | D     | G     | G     :|

          D                             G
Verse 2   I, I wish you could swim
                    D                           G
          Like the dolphins, like dolphins can swim.
                      C                                 D
          Though nothing, nothing will keep us together,
                     Am          Em                D
          We can beat them,       for ever and ever
                              C       G              D
          Oh we can be heroes,     just for one day.
```

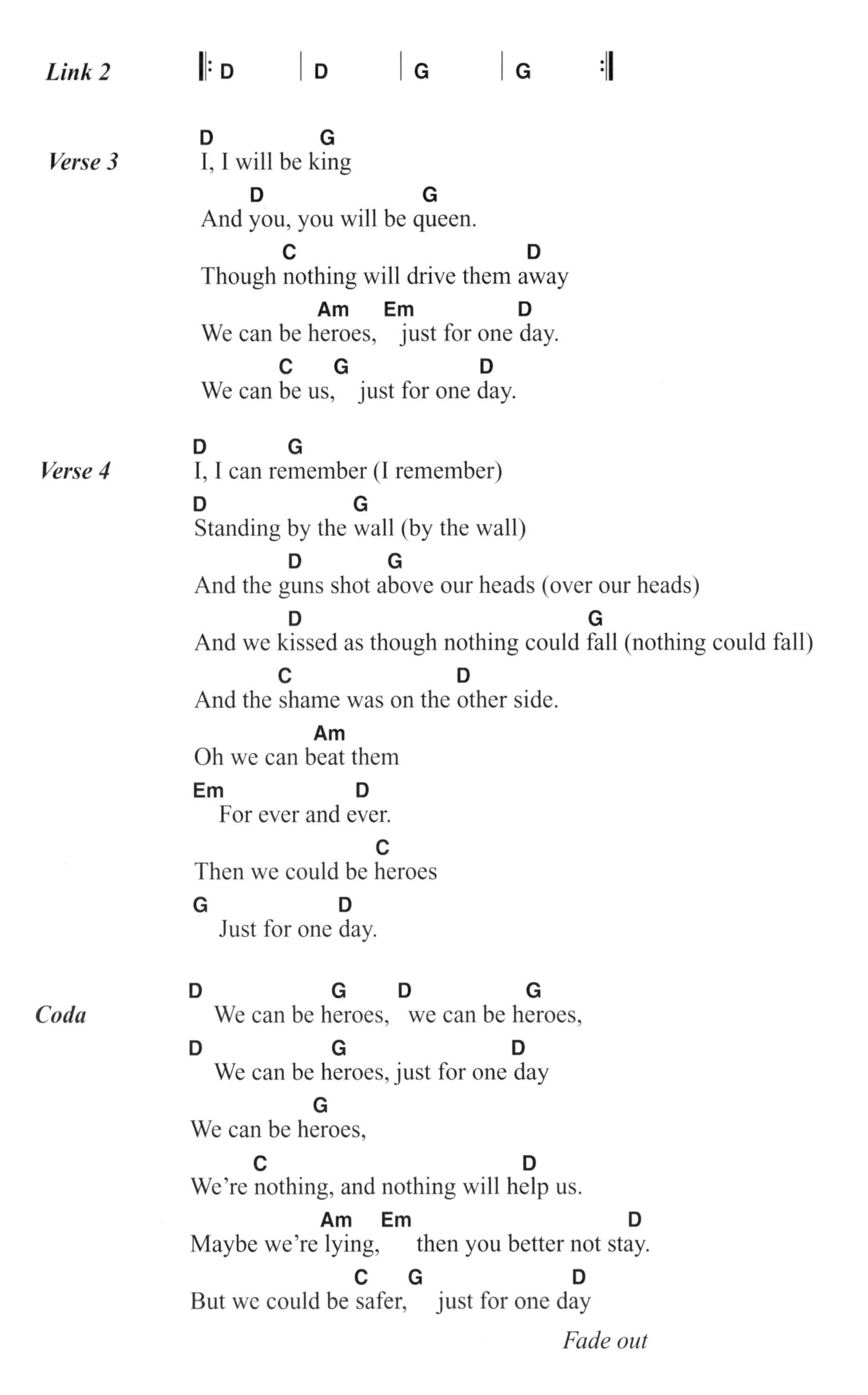
Link 2
|: D | D | G | G :|
Verse 3
D G
I, I will be king
D G
And you, you will be queen.
C D
Though nothing will drive them away
Am Em D
We can be heroes, just for one day.
C G D
We can be us, just for one day.
Verse 4
D G
I, I can remember (I remember)
D G
Standing by the wall (by the wall)
D G
And the guns shot above our heads (over our heads)
D G
And we kissed as though nothing could fall (nothing could fall)
C D
And the shame was on the other side.
Am
Oh we can beat them
Em D
For ever and ever.
C
Then we could be heroes
G D
Just for one day.
Coda
D G D G
We can be heroes, we can be heroes,
D G D
We can be heroes, just for one day
G
We can be heroes,
C D
We're nothing, and nothing will help us.
Am Em D
Maybe we're lying, then you better not stay.
C G D
But we could be safer, just for one day
Fade out

Brown Eyed Girl

Words & Music by
Van Morrison

```
Intro       | G      | C      | G      | D      |

            | G      | C      | G      | D      ||


            G                  C
Verse 1        Hey, where did we go
            G                 D
               Days when the rains came?
            G              C
               Down in the hollow,
            G          D
               Playing a new game.
            G                  C
               Laughing and a runnin', hey hey,
            G                  D
               Skipping and a - jumpin'
            G              C
               In the misty morning fog with
            G            D
               Our, our hearts a - thumpin' and


            C     D7                   G    Em
Chorus 1    You,     my brown eyed girl.
            C               D7               G    D
              And you, my      brown eyed girl.
```

Verse 2

```
G                   C
   And what ever happened
G                    D
   To Tuesday and so slow?
G                        C
   Going down to the old mine
       G         D
With a   transistor radio.
G                   C
   Standing in the sunlight laughing,
G                    D
   Hiding behind a rainbow's wall.
G                   C
   Slipping and a - sliding
G                 D
   All along the waterfall with
```

Chorus 2

```
C    D7                   G    Em
You,    my brown eyed girl.
C            D7             G   D7
   You, my      brown eyed girl.

Do you remember when
              G
We used to sing
           C
Sha la la la la la la,
G             D7
La la la la de da.

Just like that
G         C
  Sha la la la la la la,
G             D7
La la la la de da,
      (G)
La de da.
```

Link

| G | G | G | G | G | C | G | D ||

Verse 3

```
G              C
   So hard to find my way
G                  D
   Now that I'm all on my own
G              C
   I saw you just the other day
G            D
   My how you have grown
G                       C
   Cast my memory back there, Lord
G                   D
   Sometimes I'm overcome thinkin' about it
G                       C
   Makin' love in the green grass
G                D
   Behind the stadium with
```

Chorus 3

```
C    D7                  G    Em
You,    my brown eyed girl
C                D7             G    D7
   And you, my    brown eyed girl.

Do you remember when
              G
We used to sing
 G            C
|:  Sha la la la la la la,
G              D7
La la la la de da.
(Lying in the green grass)
G             C
   Sha la la la la la la,
G              D7
La la la la de da,   :|   Repeat ad lib. to fade
```

The Great Beyond

Words & Music by
Peter Buck, Michael Stipe & Michael Mills

D7sus2 Dsus2 C C/B Am G D Em(add9)

Tune guitar slightly sharp

Intro | D7sus2 | Dsus2 | D7sus2 | Dsus2 ||

Verse 1

```
D7sus2                  Dsus2            D7sus2          Dsus2
   I've watched the stars fall silent from your eyes
D7sus2                 Dsus2             D7sus2  Dsus2
All the sights that I have seen.
D7sus2          Dsus2              D7sus2                   Dsus2
   I can't be - lieve that I be - lieved I wished that you could see
D7sus2                            Dsus2
There's a new planet in the solar system
D7sus2               Dsus2
There is nothing up my sleeve.
```

Pre-chorus 1

```
C      C/B         Am
   I'm pushing an elephant up the stairs,
C      C/B         Am
   I'm tossing up punch lines that were never there,
C            C/B         Am
   Over my shoulder a piano falls
G
Crashing to the ground.
```

Verse 2

```
D7sus2       Dsus2         D7sus2      Dsus2
   In all this talk of time, talk is fine
    D7sus2          Dsus2         D7sus2  Dsus2
But I don't want to stay around.
D7sus2              Dsus2              D7sus2
   Why can't we pantomime, just close our eyes
    Dsus2
And sleep sweet dreams?
D7sus2               Dsus2                D7sus2  Dsus2
Me and you with wings on our feet.
```

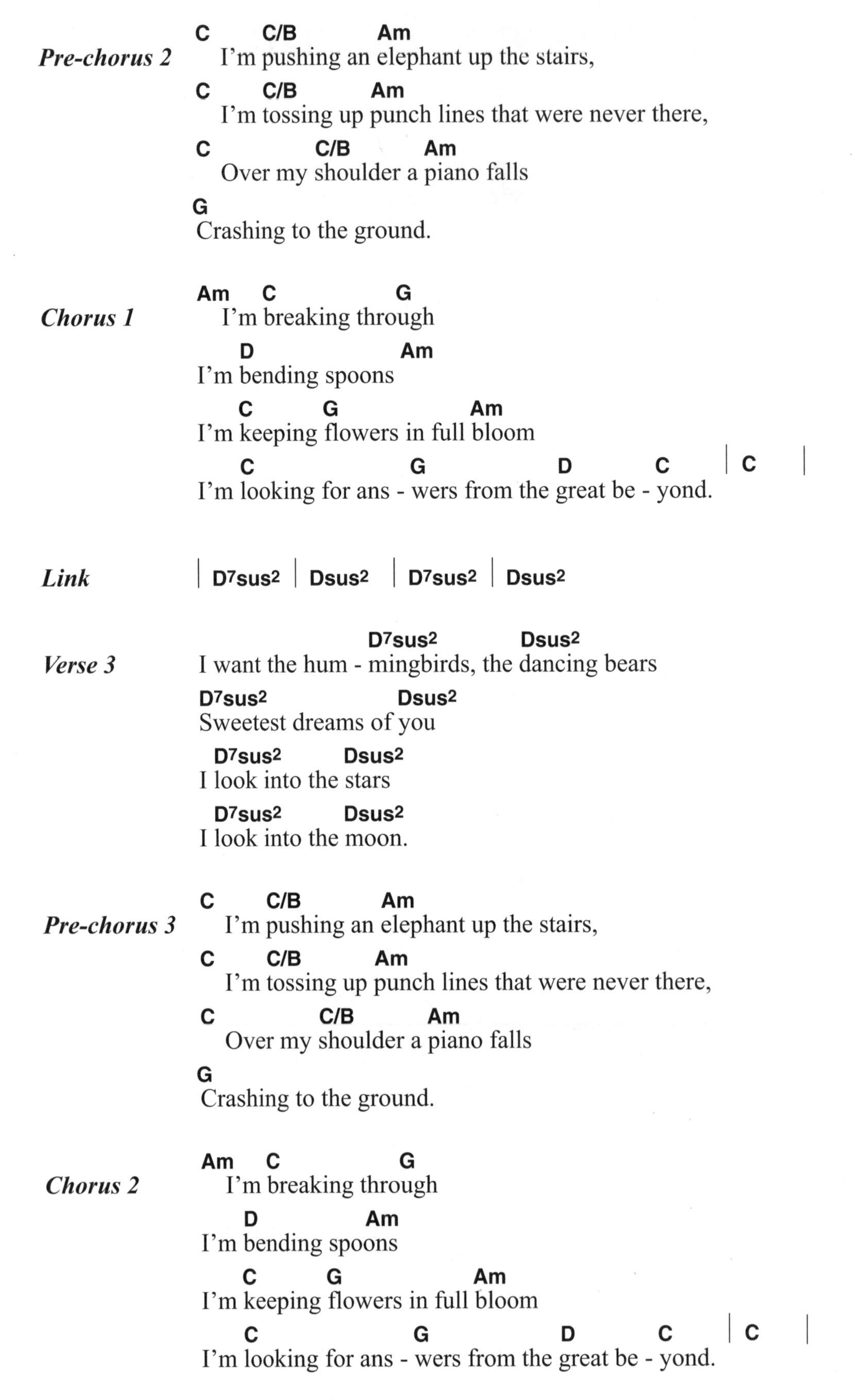

Pre-chorus 2

C C/B Am
I'm pushing an elephant up the stairs,
C C/B Am
I'm tossing up punch lines that were never there,
C C/B Am
Over my shoulder a piano falls
G
Crashing to the ground.

Chorus 1

Am C G
I'm breaking through
D Am
I'm bending spoons
C G Am
I'm keeping flowers in full bloom
C G D C | C |
I'm looking for ans - wers from the great be - yond.

Link

| D7sus2 | Dsus2 | D7sus2 | Dsus2

Verse 3

D7sus2 Dsus2
I want the hum - mingbirds, the dancing bears
D7sus2 Dsus2
Sweetest dreams of you
D7sus2 Dsus2
I look into the stars
D7sus2 Dsus2
I look into the moon.

Pre-chorus 3

C C/B Am
I'm pushing an elephant up the stairs,
C C/B Am
I'm tossing up punch lines that were never there,
C C/B Am
Over my shoulder a piano falls
G
Crashing to the ground.

Chorus 2

Am C G
I'm breaking through
D Am
I'm bending spoons
C G Am
I'm keeping flowers in full bloom
C G D C | C |
I'm looking for ans - wers from the great be - yond.

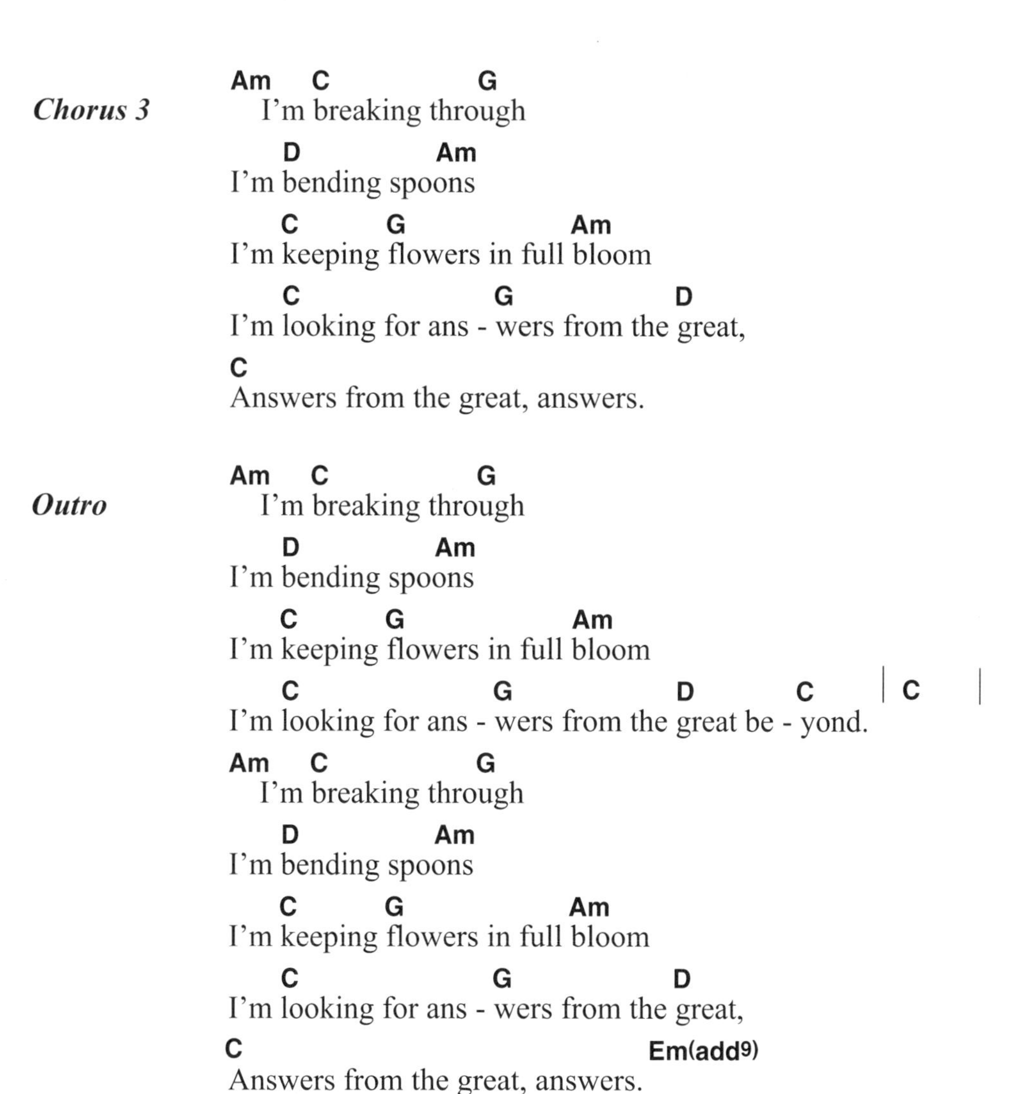
Chorus 3
Am C G
I'm breaking through
D Am
I'm bending spoons
C G Am
I'm keeping flowers in full bloom
C G D
I'm looking for ans - wers from the great,
C
Answers from the great, answers.
Outro
Am C G
I'm breaking through
D Am
I'm bending spoons
C G Am
I'm keeping flowers in full bloom
C G D C | C |
I'm looking for ans - wers from the great be - yond.
Am C G
I'm breaking through
D Am
I'm bending spoons
C G Am
I'm keeping flowers in full bloom
C G D
I'm looking for ans - wers from the great,
C Em(add9)
Answers from the great, answers.

Purple Rain

Words & Music by
Prince

B♭add9/D Gm7add11 Fsus2 E♭maj9 B♭sus2 F B♭ E♭

Intro | B♭add9/D | Gm7add11 | Fsus2 | E♭maj7 ||

Verse 1

B♭sus2 Gm7add11
I never meant 2 cause U any sorrow,
Fsus2 E♭maj9
I never meant 2 cause U any pain.
B♭sus2 Gm7add11
I only wanted one time 2 see U laughing,
F B♭
I only want 2 see U laughing in the purple rain.

Chorus 1

N.C. E♭ B♭sus2
Purple rain, purple rain, purple rain, purple rain,
Gm7add11 F
Purple rain, purple rain.
B♭
I only want 2 see U bathing in the purple rain.

Verse 2

N.C. B♭sus2 Gm7add11
I never wanted 2 be your weekend lover,
Fsus2 E♭maj9
I only wanted 2 be some kind of friend, hey.
B♭sus2 Gm7add11
Baby, I could never steal U from another.
F B♭
It's such a shame our friendship had 2 end.

Chorus 2

N.C. E♭ B♭sus2
Purple rain, purple rain, purple rain, purple rain,
Gm7add11 F
Purple rain, purple rain.
B♭
I only want 2 see U underneath the purple rain.

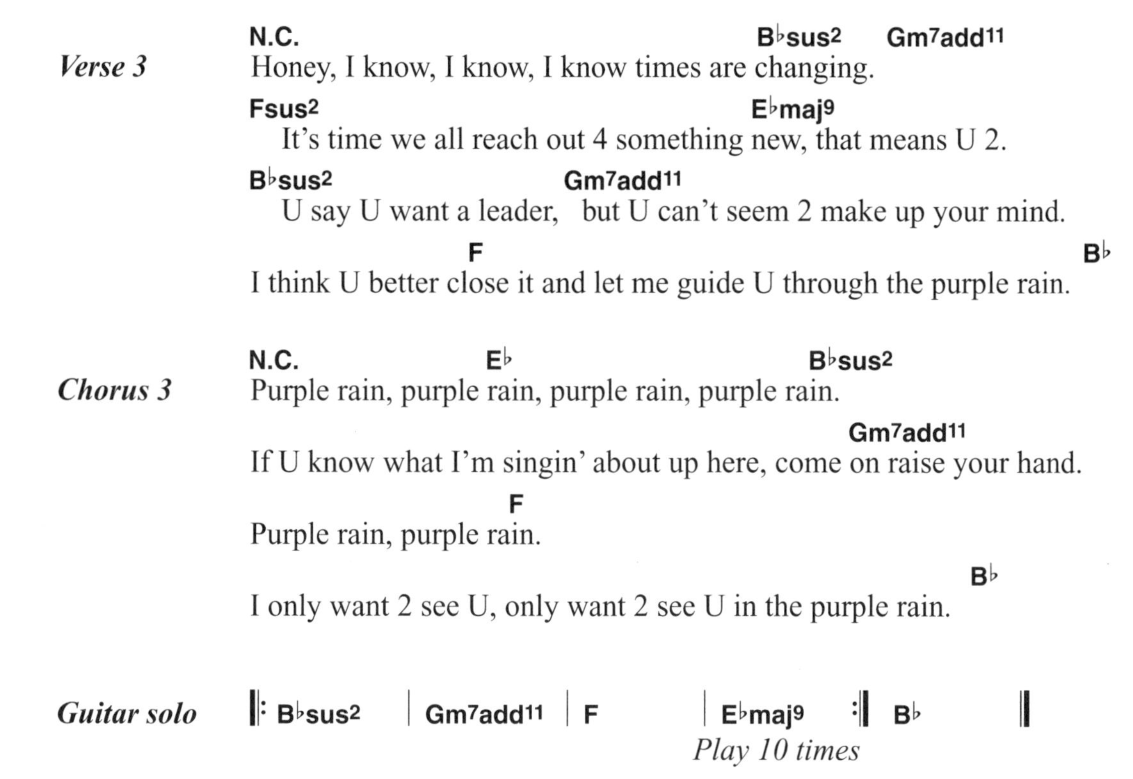

Verse 3

```
N.C.                                          B♭sus2    Gm7add11
Honey, I know, I know, I know times are changing.
Fsus2                                        E♭maj9
   It's time we all reach out 4 something new, that means U 2.
B♭sus2                       Gm7add11
   U say U want a leader,   but U can't seem 2 make up your mind.
                     F                                               B♭
I think U better close it and let me guide U through the purple rain.
```

Chorus 3

```
N.C.                   E♭                            B♭sus2
Purple rain, purple rain, purple rain, purple rain.
                                                     Gm7add11
If U know what I'm singin' about up here, come on raise your hand.
                        F
Purple rain, purple rain.
                                                          B♭
I only want 2 see U, only want 2 see U in the purple rain.
```

Guitar solo

```
𝄆 B♭sus2 | Gm7add11 | F | E♭maj9 𝄇 B♭ ‖
                  Play 10 times
```

The River Of Dreams

Words & Music by
Billy Joel

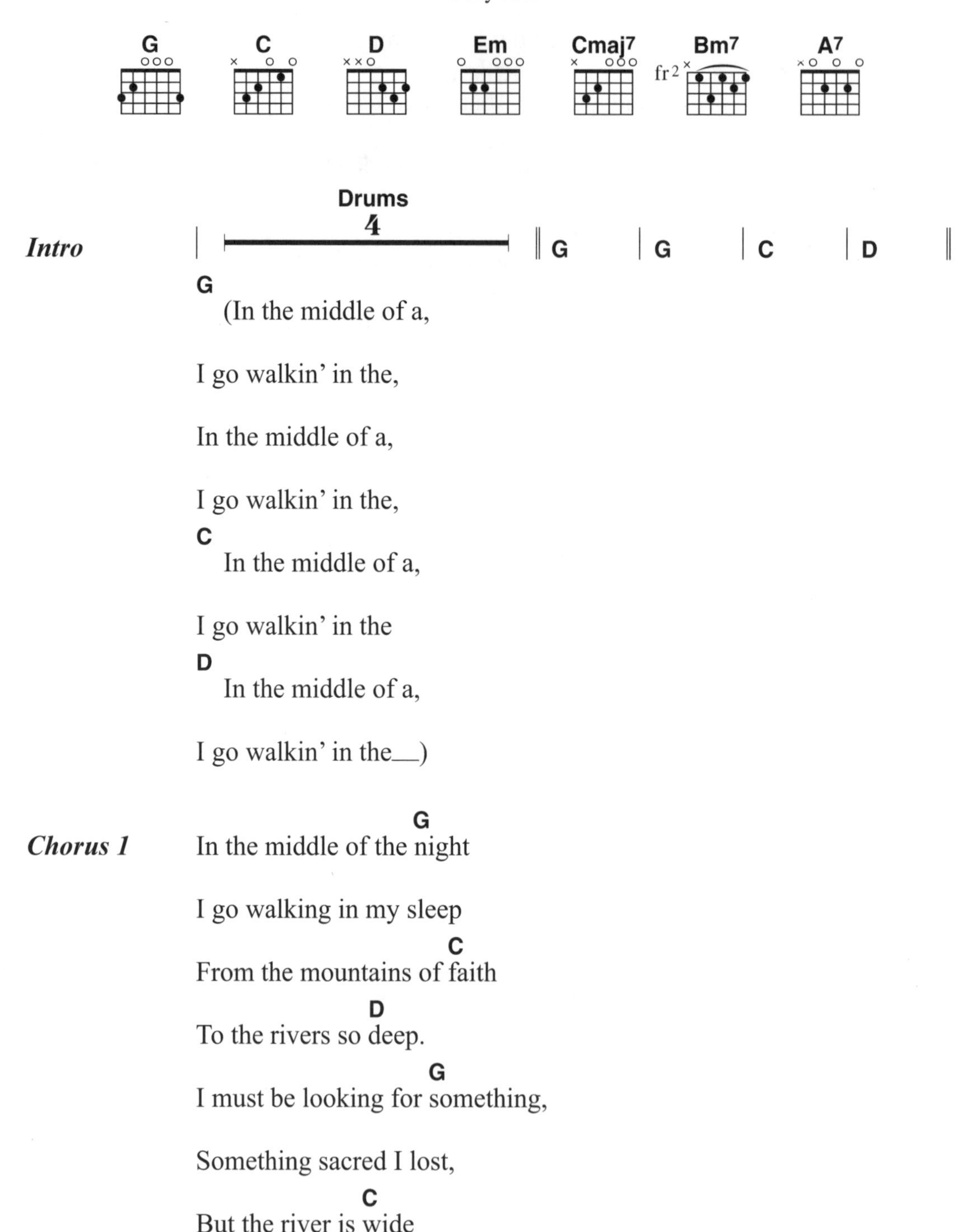

Drums
4

Intro | 4 || G | G | C | D ||

G
(In the middle of a,

I go walkin' in the,

In the middle of a,

I go walkin' in the,

C
In the middle of a,

I go walkin' in the

D
In the middle of a,

I go walkin' in the__)

Chorus 1

G
In the middle of the night

I go walking in my sleep

C
From the mountains of faith

D
To the rivers so deep.

G
I must be looking for something,

Something sacred I lost,

C
But the river is wide

D
And it's too hard to cross.

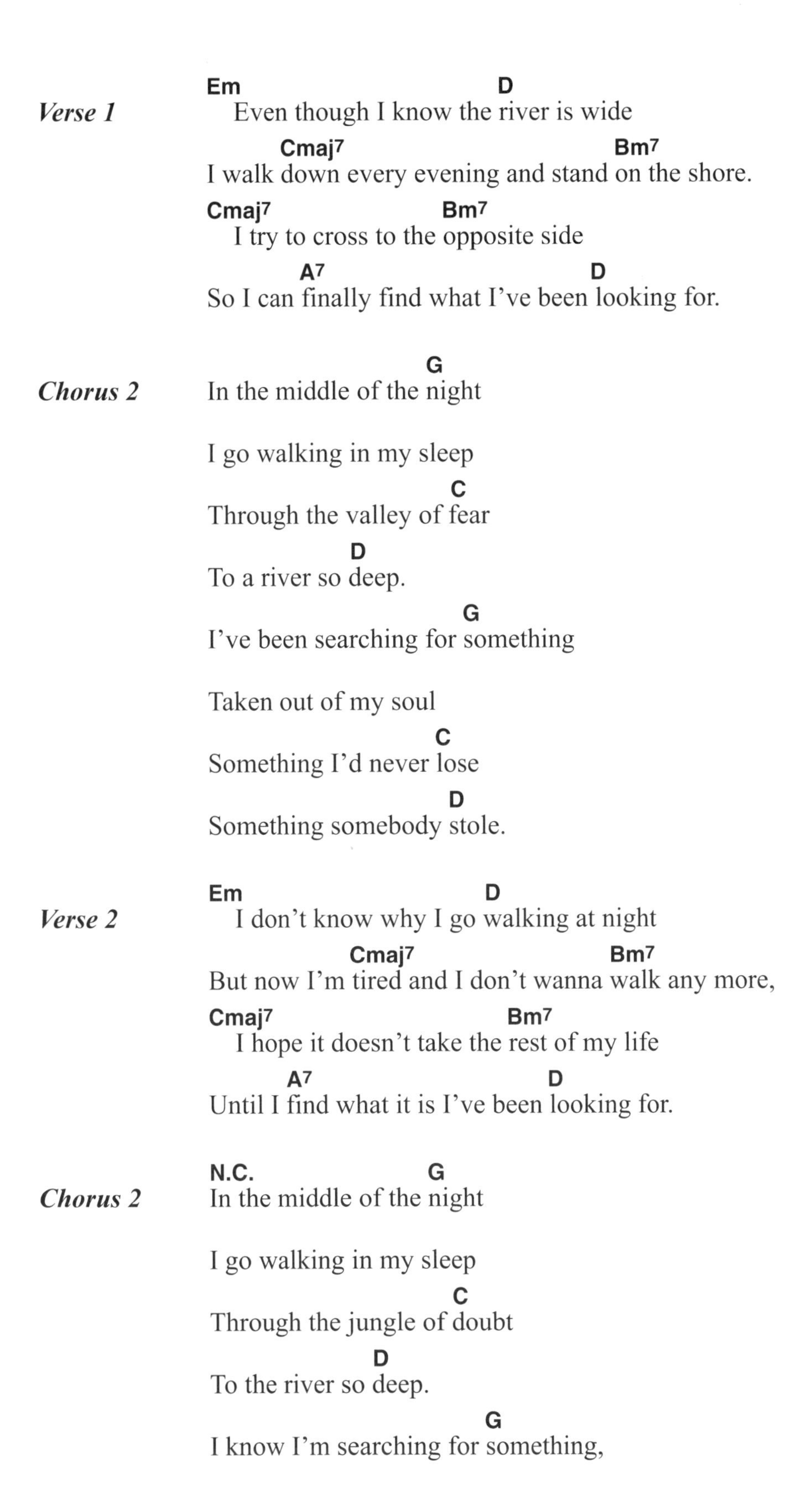

Verse 1

Em D
Even though I know the river is wide

Cmaj7 Bm7
I walk down every evening and stand on the shore.

Cmaj7 Bm7
I try to cross to the opposite side

A7 D
So I can finally find what I've been looking for.

Chorus 2

G
In the middle of the night

I go walking in my sleep

C
Through the valley of fear

D
To a river so deep.

G
I've been searching for something

Taken out of my soul

C
Something I'd never lose

D
Something somebody stole.

Verse 2

Em D
I don't know why I go walking at night

Cmaj7 Bm7
But now I'm tired and I don't wanna walk any more,

Cmaj7 Bm7
I hope it doesn't take the rest of my life

A7 D
Until I find what it is I've been looking for.

Chorus 2

N.C. G
In the middle of the night

I go walking in my sleep

C
Through the jungle of doubt

D
To the river so deep.

G
I know I'm searching for something,

cont.

Something so undefined,

C
And it can only be seen

D
By the eyes of the blind.

G
In the middle of the night.

Middle

(I go walkin' in the,

In the middle of a,

I go walkin' in the,

In the middle of a,

C
I go walkin' in the

In the middle of a,

D
I go walkin' in the,

In the middle of a,

G
I go walkin' in the

In the middle of a,

I go walkin' in the,

In the middle of a,

I go walkin' in the,

In the middle of a,

C
I go walkin' in the,

In the middle of a,

D
I go walkin' in the,

In the middle of a,)

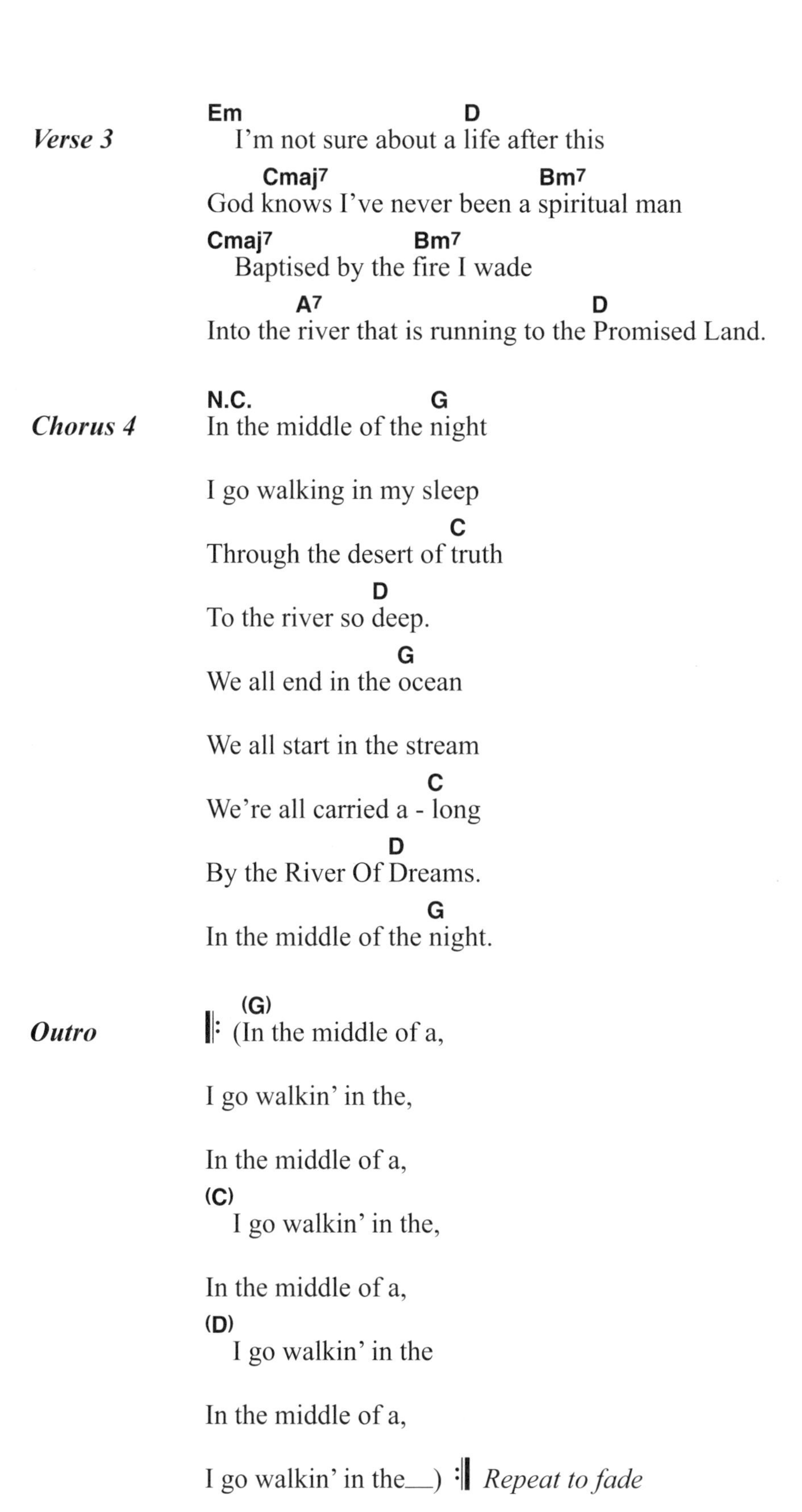

Verse 3

Em D
I'm not sure about a life after this

Cmaj7 Bm7
God knows I've never been a spiritual man

Cmaj7 Bm7
Baptised by the fire I wade

A7 D
Into the river that is running to the Promised Land.

Chorus 4

N.C. G
In the middle of the night

I go walking in my sleep

C
Through the desert of truth

D
To the river so deep.

G
We all end in the ocean

We all start in the stream

C
We're all carried a - long

D
By the River Of Dreams.

G
In the middle of the night.

Outro

(G)
𝄆 (In the middle of a,

I go walkin' in the,

In the middle of a,

(C)
I go walkin' in the,

In the middle of a,

(D)
I go walkin' in the

In the middle of a,

I go walkin' in the__) 𝄇 *Repeat to fade*

The Road To Hell

Words & Music by
Chris Rea

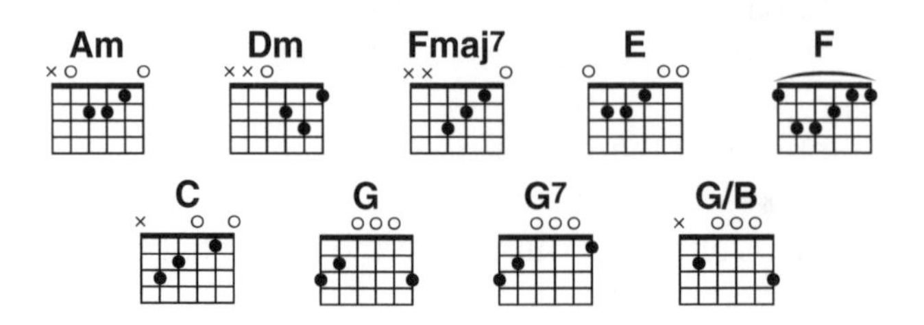

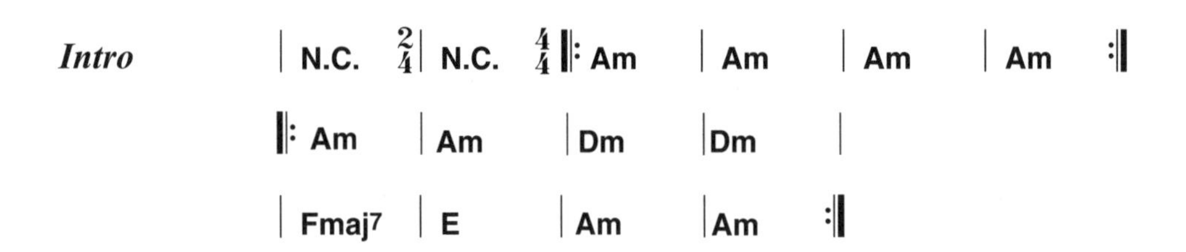

Verse 1

```
               Am
Well I'm standing by a river
             Dm
But the water doesn't flow
  F                           E          Am
It boils with every poison   you can think of.
              Am
And I'm underneath the streetlight
             Dm
But the light of joy I know
  F                     E                     Am
Is scared beyond belief   way down in the sha - dows.
                C
And the per - verted fear of violence
               G
Chokes the smile on every face
     F                                E
And common sense is ringing out the bells.
Am                             Dm
   This ain't no technological breakdown
       F       E       Am
Oh no,  this is the road to Hell.
```

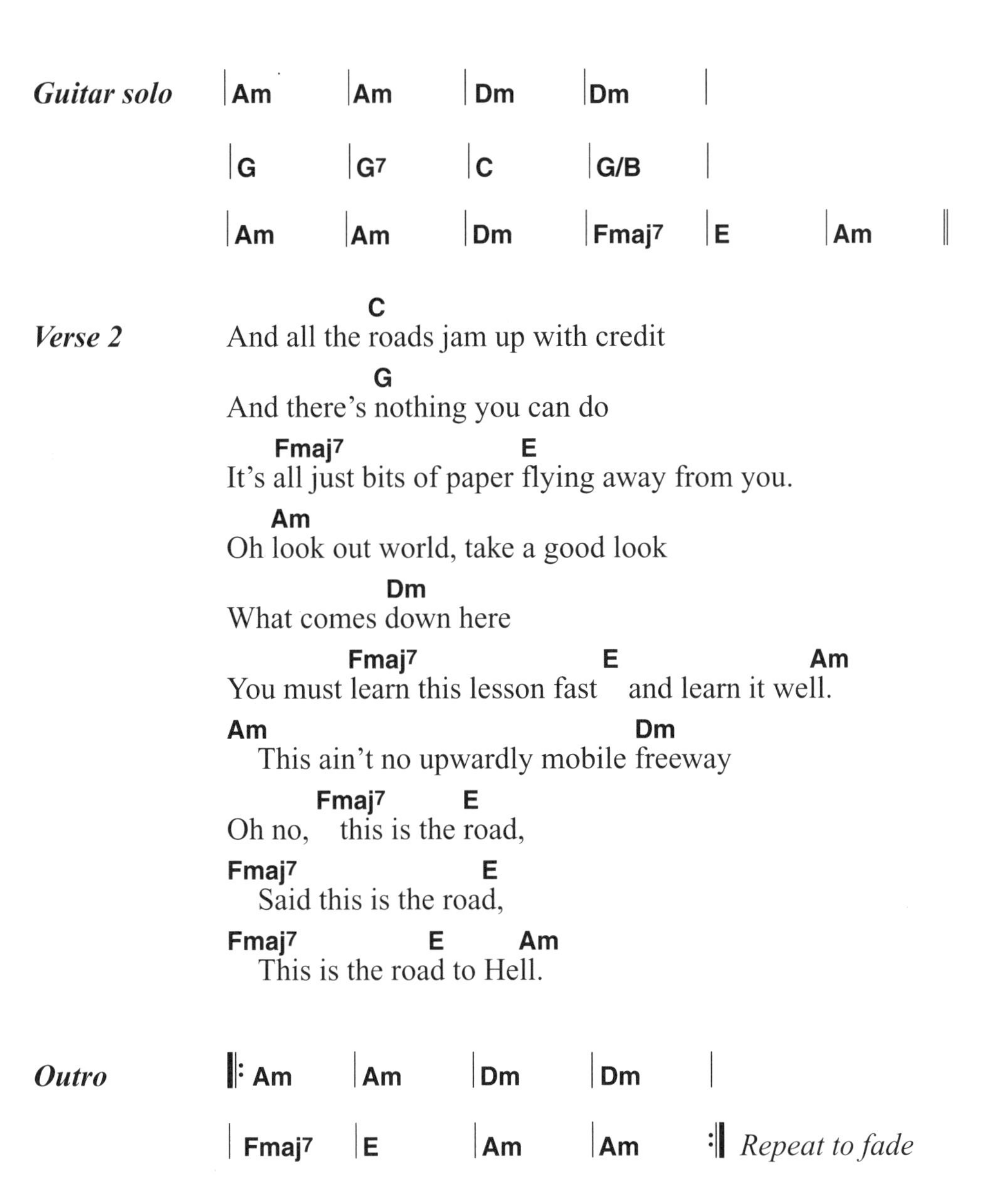

Guitar solo | Am | Am | Dm | Dm |

| G | G7 | C | G/B |

| Am | Am | Dm | Fmaj7 | E | Am ||

Verse 2

C
And all the roads jam up with credit
G
And there's nothing you can do
Fmaj7 E
It's all just bits of paper flying away from you.
Am
Oh look out world, take a good look
Dm
What comes down here
Fmaj7 E Am
You must learn this lesson fast and learn it well.
Am Dm
This ain't no upwardly mobile freeway
Fmaj7 E
Oh no, this is the road,
Fmaj7 E
Said this is the road,
Fmaj7 E Am
This is the road to Hell.

Outro |: Am | Am | Dm | Dm |

| Fmaj7 | E | Am | Am :| *Repeat to fade*

Don't Stop

Words & Music by
Christine McVie

E A/E D A B E9

Intro | E A/E | E A/E | E A/E | E A/E :|

Verse 1

```
E          D               A
    If you wake up and don't want to smile;
E       D              A
    If it takes just a little while,
E                D     A
    Open your eyes, look at the day
B
You'll see things in a different way.
```

Chorus 1

```
E       E9    A
Don't stop thinking about tomorrow,
E       E9     A
Don't stop, it'll soon be here:
E        E9 A
    It'll be better than before.
B
Yesterday's gone, yesterday's gone.
```

Link 1 | E D | A | E D | A ||

Verse 2

```
E              D              A
    Why not think about times to come
E              D        A
    And not about the things that you've done?
E           D       A
    If your life was bad for you
B
    Just think what tomorrow will do.
```

Chorus 2 As Chorus 1

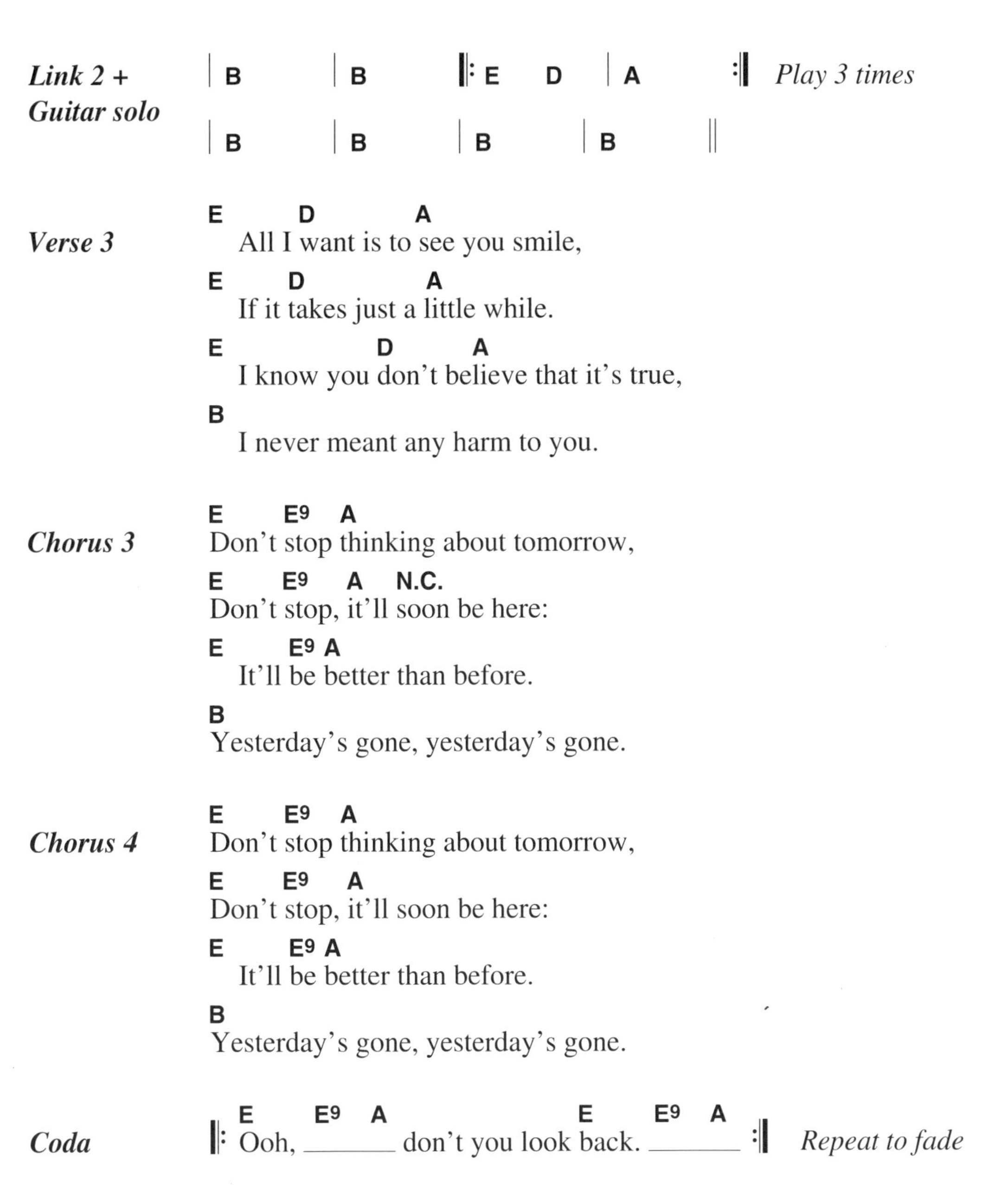
Link 2 +
Guitar solo
| B | B |: E D | A :| Play 3 times
| B | B | B | B ||
Verse 3
E D A
All I want is to see you smile,
E D A
If it takes just a little while.
E D A
I know you don't believe that it's true,
B
I never meant any harm to you.
Chorus 3
E E9 A
Don't stop thinking about tomorrow,
E E9 A N.C.
Don't stop, it'll soon be here:
E E9 A
It'll be better than before.
B
Yesterday's gone, yesterday's gone.
Chorus 4
E E9 A
Don't stop thinking about tomorrow,
E E9 A
Don't stop, it'll soon be here:
E E9 A
It'll be better than before.
B
Yesterday's gone, yesterday's gone.
Coda
E E9 A E E9 A
|: Ooh, ______ don't you look back. ______ :| Repeat to fade

Running Up That Hill

Words & Music by
Kate Bush

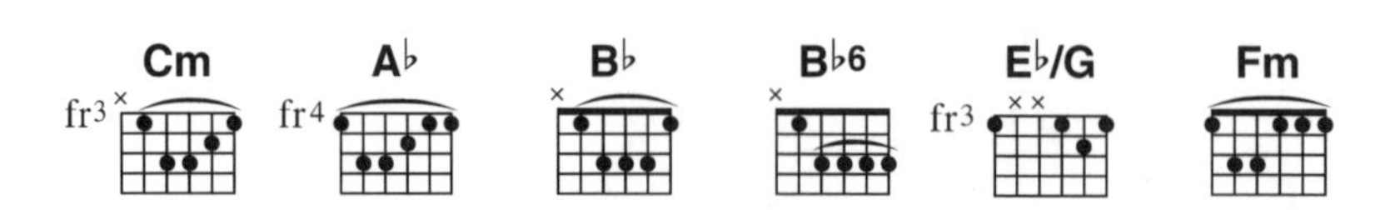

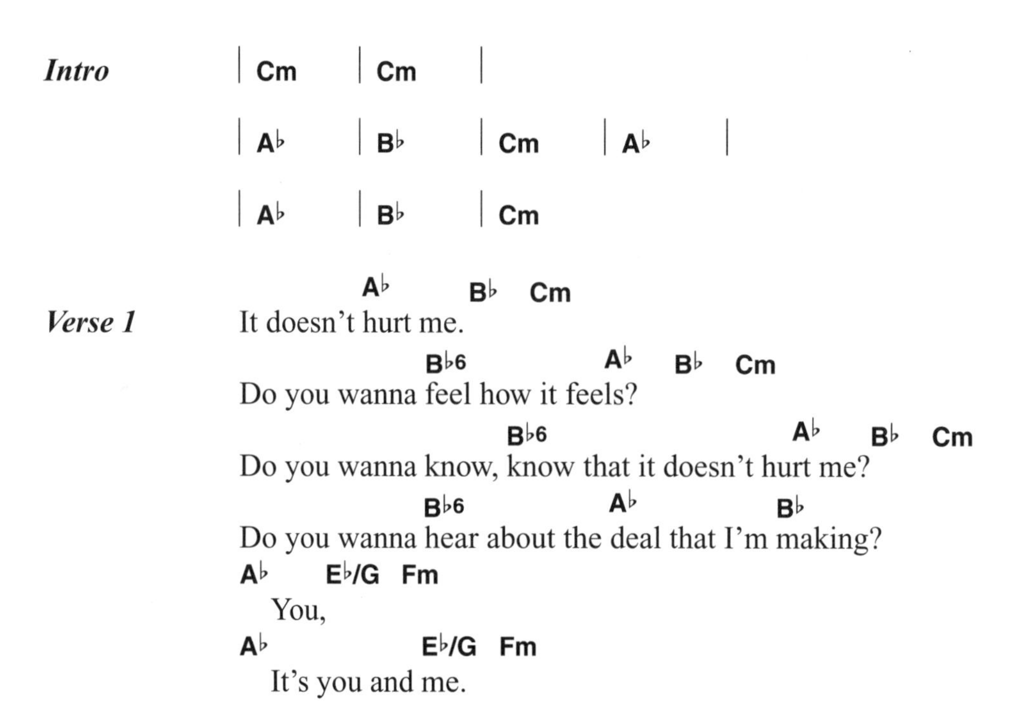

Intro

| Cm | Cm |

| A♭ | B♭ | Cm | A♭ |

| A♭ | B♭ | Cm

Verse 1

```
           A♭        B♭   Cm
It doesn't hurt me.
                 B♭6             A♭    B♭   Cm
Do you wanna feel how it feels?
                        B♭6                    A♭     B♭   Cm
Do you wanna know, know that it doesn't hurt me?
                 B♭6           A♭           B♭
Do you wanna hear about the deal that I'm making?
A♭      E♭/G  Fm
   You,
A♭               E♭/G  Fm
   It's you and me.
```

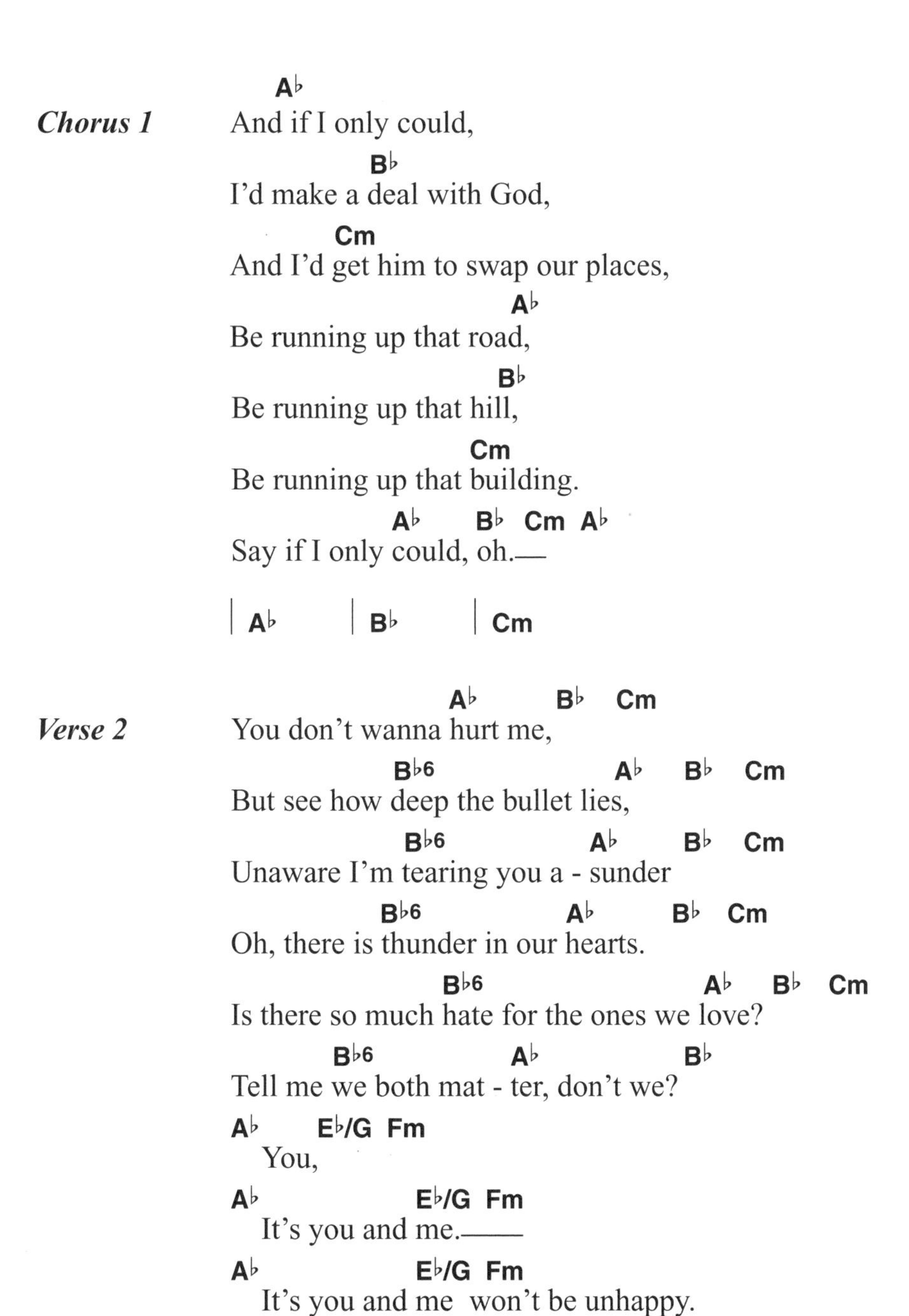

```
                 A♭
Chorus 1    And if I only could,
                        B♭
            I'd make a deal with God,
                      Cm
            And I'd get him to swap our places,
                                    A♭
            Be running up that road,
                                   B♭
            Be running up that hill,
                                 Cm
            Be running up that building.
                            A♭      B♭   Cm  A♭
            Say if I only could, oh.—

            | A♭      | B♭      | Cm


                                A♭      B♭   Cm
Verse 2     You don't wanna hurt me,
                           B♭6               A♭    B♭   Cm
            But see how deep the bullet lies,
                            B♭6          A♭      B♭   Cm
            Unaware I'm tearing you a - sunder
                          B♭6           A♭        B♭   Cm
            Oh, there is thunder in our hearts.
                              B♭6                     A♭    B♭   Cm
            Is there so much hate for the ones we love?
                        B♭6         A♭          B♭
            Tell me we both mat - ter, don't we?
            A♭      E♭/G  Fm
              You,
            A♭            E♭/G  Fm
              It's you and me.——
            A♭            E♭/G  Fm
              It's you and me  won't be unhappy.
```

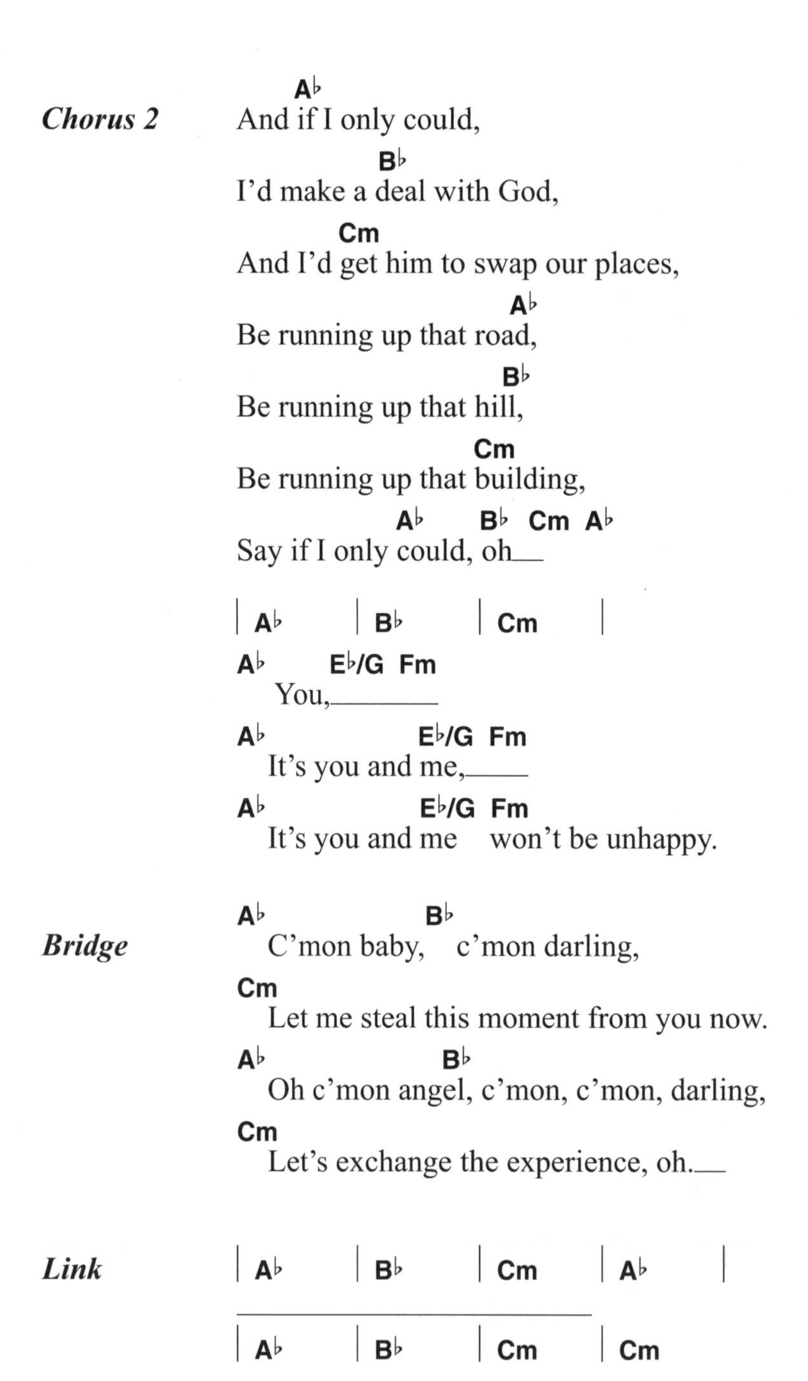

Chorus 2

```
      A♭
And if I only could,
               B♭
I'd make a deal with God,
           Cm
And I'd get him to swap our places,
                       A♭
Be running up that road,
                       B♭
Be running up that hill,
                    Cm
Be running up that building,
              A♭      B♭  Cm  A♭
Say if I only could, oh__

| A♭      | B♭      | Cm      |

A♭      E♭/G  Fm
   You,_______
A♭               E♭/G  Fm
  It's you and me,____
A♭               E♭/G  Fm
  It's you and me    won't be unhappy.
```

Bridge

```
A♭              B♭
  C'mon baby,    c'mon darling,
Cm
  Let me steal this moment from you now.
A♭                B♭
  Oh c'mon angel, c'mon, c'mon, darling,
Cm
  Let's exchange the experience, oh.__
```

Link

```
| A♭      | B♭      | Cm      | A♭      |
_____________________________
| A♭      | B♭      | Cm      | Cm
```

Chorus 3

𝄆 And if I only (A♭)could,
I'd make a deal with (B♭)God,
And I'd get him to (Cm)swap our places,
Be running up that (A♭)road,
Be running up that (B♭)hill,
With no (Cm)problems. 𝄇
Said if I only (A♭)could,
I'd make a deal with (B♭)God,
And I'd get him to (Cm)swap our places,
Be running up that (A♭)road,
Be running up that (B♭)hill,
With no (Cm)problems.
Say if I only (A♭)could | A♭
Be running up that (B♭)hill | B♭
With no (Cm)problems... | Cm | Cm | Cm |

Outro

(Cm)If I only could, I'd be running up that hill.
(Cm)If I only could, I'd be running up that hill.

You're So Vain

Words & Music by
Carly Simon

Am7 F G Em C Dm7 Am G7add13

Intro

(Am7)
Whispered: Son of a gun...

| Am7 | Am7 | Am7 | Am7 | Am7 | Am7 ||

Verse 1

Am7
You walked into the party
F Am7
Like you were walking onto a yacht,

Your hat strategically dipped below one eye,
F Am7
Your scarf it was apricot.
F G Em Am7
You had one eye in the mirror as
F C
You watched yourself gavotte.
G F
And all the girls dreamed that they'd be your partner,

They'd be your partner and...

Chorus 1

C
You're so vain,
Dm7 C
You probably think this song is about you.
Am
You're so vain (you're so vain)
F G7add13
I bet you think this song is about you,

Don't you, don't you?

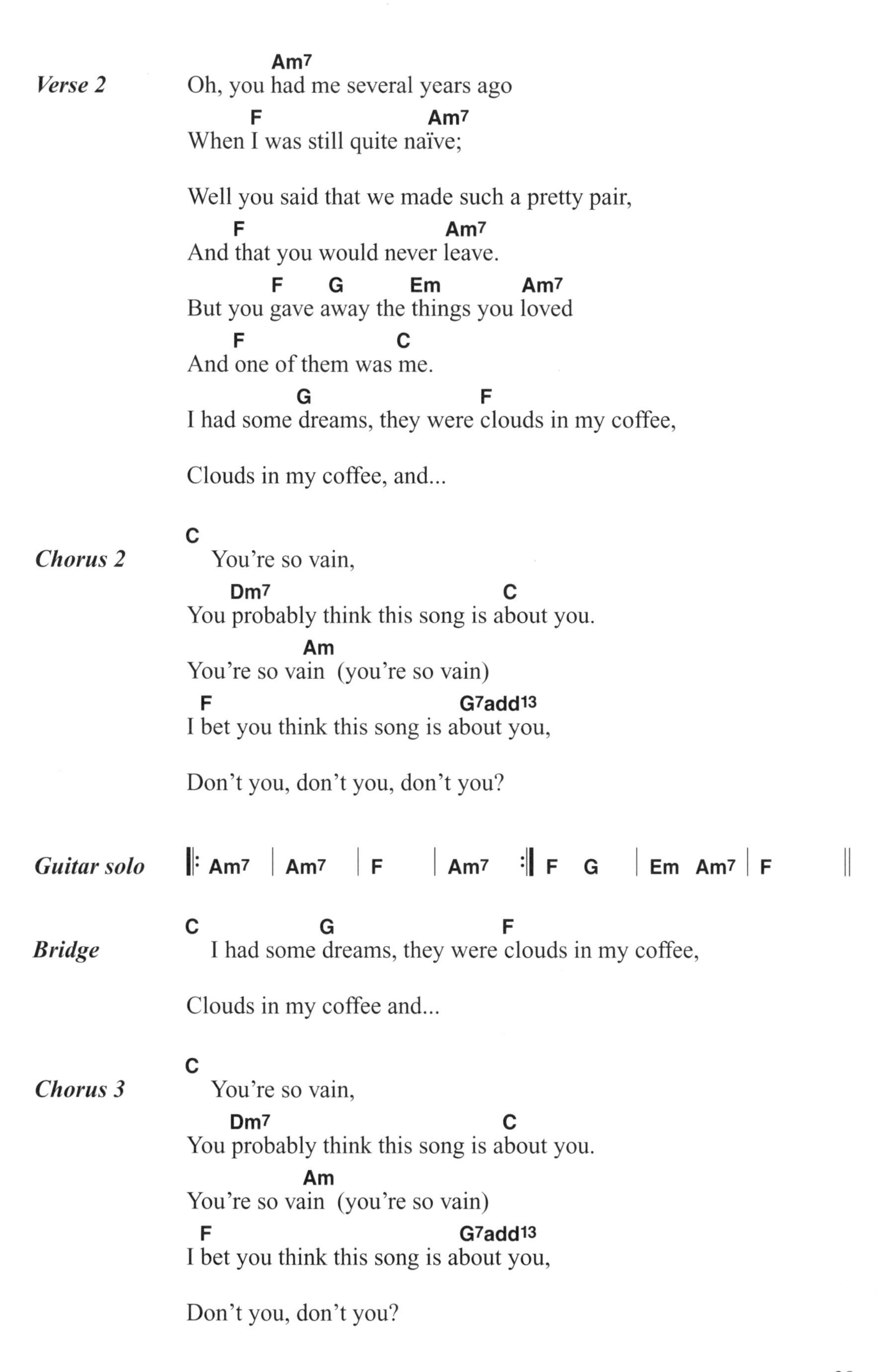

Verse 2

Am7
Oh, you had me several years ago

F Am7
When I was still quite naïve;

Well you said that we made such a pretty pair,

F Am7
And that you would never leave.

F G Em Am7
But you gave away the things you loved

F C
And one of them was me.

G F
I had some dreams, they were clouds in my coffee,

Clouds in my coffee, and...

Chorus 2

C
You're so vain,

Dm7 C
You probably think this song is about you.

Am
You're so vain (you're so vain)

F G7add13
I bet you think this song is about you,

Don't you, don't you, don't you?

Guitar solo

𝄆 Am7 | Am7 | F | Am7 𝄇 F G | Em Am7 | F ‖

Bridge

C G F
I had some dreams, they were clouds in my coffee,

Clouds in my coffee and...

Chorus 3

C
You're so vain,

Dm7 C
You probably think this song is about you.

Am
You're so vain (you're so vain)

F G7add13
I bet you think this song is about you,

Don't you, don't you?

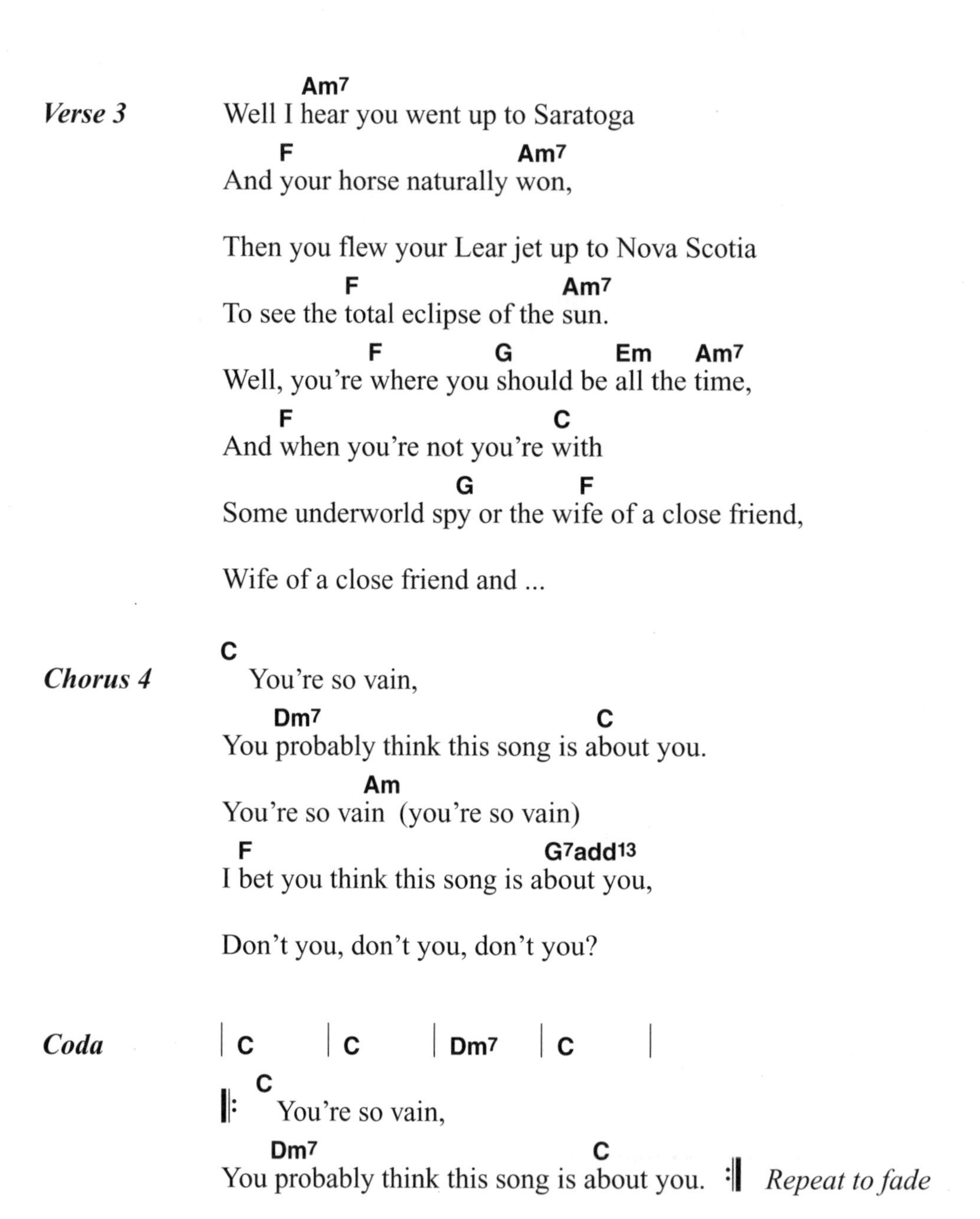

Verse 3

```
          Am7
Well I hear you went up to Saratoga
    F                    Am7
And your horse naturally won,

Then you flew your Lear jet up to Nova Scotia
         F                  Am7
To see the total eclipse of the sun.
          F          G         Em     Am7
Well, you're where you should be all the time,
    F                    C
And when you're not you're with
                   G         F
Some underworld spy or the wife of a close friend,

Wife of a close friend and ...
```

Chorus 4

```
C
  You're so vain,
   Dm7                        C
You probably think this song is about you.
         Am
You're so vain  (you're so vain)
 F                        G7add13
I bet you think this song is about you,

Don't you, don't you, don't you?
```

Coda

```
| C     | C     | Dm7   | C     |

||: C
     You're so vain,
   Dm7                        C
You probably think this song is about you.  :||  Repeat to fade
```

No Woman, No Cry

Words & Music by
Vincent Ford

C C/B Am F G Em Dm Cadd9

Capo first fret

```
Intro       ||: C   C/B | Am   F | C   F | C   G :||

            C     C/B           Am   F
Chorus 1       No woman, no cry,
            C     F             C     G
               No woman, no cry,
            C     C/B           Am   F
               No woman, no cry,
            C     F             C     G
               No woman, no cry.

                          C          C/B        Am                  F
Verse 1        Say, say,   said  I remember when we used to sit
            C                   C/B            Am                F
               In the government yard in Trenchtown,
            C            C/B           Am        F
               Oba-observing the hypocrites
                     C                  G/B            Am                  F
            As they   would mingle with the good people we meet.
            C          C/B                             Am                  F
               Good friends we have had, oh good friends we've lost
            C     C/B       Am     F
               Along the way.
            C          C/B                     Am           F
               In this bright future you can't forget your past,
            C                    C/B    Am    F
               So dry your tears, I say,   and
```

```
            C     C/B        Am  F
*Chorus 2*    No woman, no cry,
            C    F           C    G
              No woman, no cry,
            C     C/B            Am          F
              Here  little darlin',   don't shed no tears,
            C    F          C   G
              No woman, no cry.

                       C            C/B     Am                F
*Verse 2*     Said, said,   said I remember when we used to sit
            C            C/B                  Am             F
              In the government yard in Trenchtown,
            C            C/B               Am             F
              And then Georgie would make the fire light
                      C            C/B                     Am       F
            As it was   log wood burnin' through the night.
            C                      C/B        Am                F
              Then we would cook corn meal porridge
            C                 C/B         Am    F
              Of which I'll share with you.
            C     C/B        Am       F
              My feet is my only carriage
            C          C/B              Am    F
              So I've got to push on through.

               C                          C/B
*Bridge*      |:    Ev'rything's gonna be alright,
            Am                        F   G
              Ev'rything's gonna be alright.  :|   Play 4 times

               C               C/B  Am F
*Chorus 3*    No woman, no cry, _
                    C             F             C    G
            No, no woman, no woman, no cry.
            C            C/B   Am           F
              Oh, little sister, don't shed no tears,
            C    F           C    G
              No woman, no cry.

*Solo*        |: C   C/B | Am   F  | C   F   | C   G   :|   Play 4 times
```

Verse 3

C G/B Am F
Said, said, said I remember when we used to sit
C G/B Am F
In the government yard in Trenchtown,
C G/B Am F
And then Georgie would make the fire light
C G/B Am F
As it was log wood burnin' through the night.
C G/B Am F
Then we would cook corn meal porridge
C G/B Am F
Of which I'll share with you.
C G/B Am F
My feet is my only carriage
C G/B Am
So I've got to push on through,
F G
But while I'm gone I mean.

Chorus 4

C G/B Am F
No woman, no cry,
C F C G
No woman, no cry,
C G/B Am F
Oh c'mon little darlin', say don't shed no tears,
C F C G
No woman, no cry, yeah!

Chorus 5

C G/B Am F
(Little darlin', don't shed no tears,
C F C G
No woman, no cry.
C F C C
Little sister, don't shed no tears,
F C G
No woman, no cry.)

Coda

| C G/B | Am F | C F | C G |

| C G/B | Am F | C F Em Dm | Cadd9 ‖

If You Leave Me Now

Words & Music by
Peter Cetera

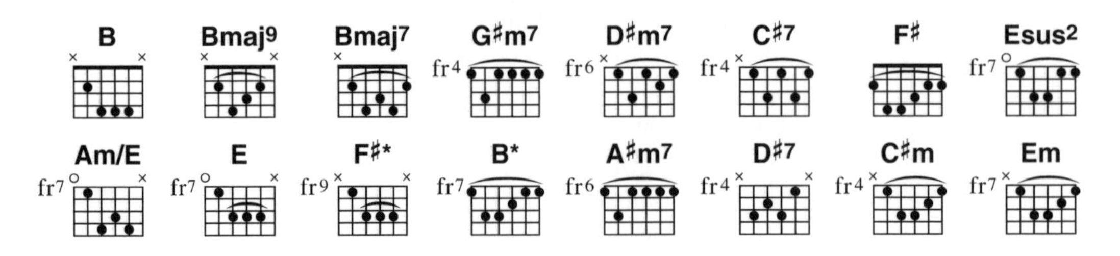

Intro

| B Bmaj9 B Bmaj9 | B Bmaj9 B |

| B Bmaj9 B Bmaj9 | B ‖
(If you)

Verse 1

Bmaj7
If you leave me now,
G♯m7 D♯m7
You'll take away the biggest part of me.
G♯m C♯7 F♯ B Bmaj9 B
Ooh— no baby, please don't go.
Bmaj7
And if you leave me now,
G♯m7 D♯m7
You'll take away the very heart of me.
G♯m7 C♯7 F♯ B
Ooh— no baby, please don't go
G♯m7 C♯m7 F♯ B Bmaj9 B
Ooh— girl, I just want you to stay.

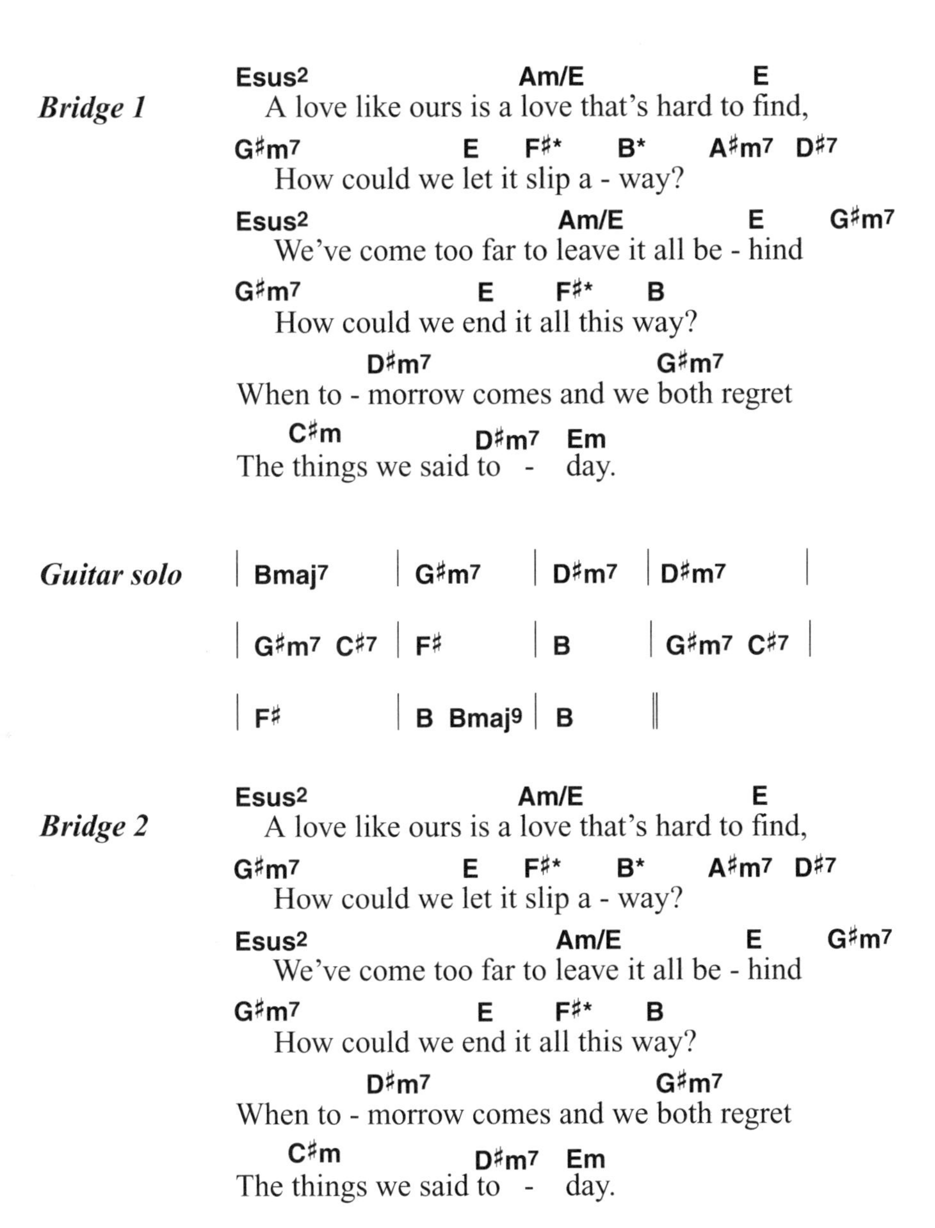
Bridge 1
Esus2 Am/E E
A love like ours is a love that's hard to find,
G♯m7 E F♯* B* A♯m7 D♯7
How could we let it slip a - way?
Esus2 Am/E E G♯m7
We've come too far to leave it all be - hind
G♯m7 E F♯* B
How could we end it all this way?
D♯m7 G♯m7
When to - morrow comes and we both regret
C♯m D♯m7 Em
The things we said to - day.
Guitar solo
Bmaj7	G♯m7	D♯m7	D♯m7
G♯m7 C♯7	F♯	B	G♯m7 C♯7
F♯	B Bmaj9	B	
Bridge 2
Esus2 Am/E E
A love like ours is a love that's hard to find,
G♯m7 E F♯* B* A♯m7 D♯7
How could we let it slip a - way?
Esus2 Am/E E G♯m7
We've come too far to leave it all be - hind
G♯m7 E F♯* B
How could we end it all this way?
D♯m7 G♯m7
When to - morrow comes and we both regret
C♯m D♯m7 Em
The things we said to - day.

Verse 2

```
           Bmaj7
If you leave me now
           G#m7                        D#m7
You'll take away the biggest part of me.
        G#m7   C#7        F#              B
Ooh—        no baby, please don't go.
```

Link 1

```
| G#m7  C#7 | F#  | B  Bmaj9  B  Bmaj9 | B  Bmaj9  B |
G#m7      C#7      F#                      B
Ooh,— girl, just got to have you by my side.
```

Link 2

```
| G#m7  C#7 | F#  | B  Bmaj9  B  Bmaj9 | B  Bmaj9  B |
     G#m7  C#7        F#            B
Ooh—      no baby, please don't go.
```

Outro

```
|: G#m7  C#7 | F#  | B  Bmaj9  B  Bmaj9 | B  Bmaj9  B |
  G#m7       C#7         F#                    B
Ooh— my, my, I just got to have your lovin'.  :|
```

Repeat to fade ad lib.

I Want To Know What Love Is

Words & Music by
Mick Jones

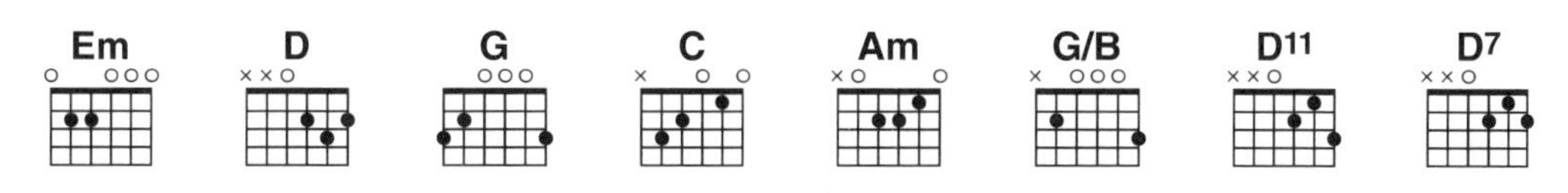

Tune guitar down a semitone

Intro | Em D | G | C Em | Em ||

Verse 1

```
Em                   D        G
   I've gotta take a little time
          C                   Em | Em     |
A little time to think things over.
Em                     D           G
   I'd better read be - tween the lines
           C                 Em | Em     |
In case I need it when I'm older.
D     Em | Em      |
   Oh.__
```

Verse 2

```
Em                     D           G
   Now this mountain I must climb,
              |C           |Em
Feels like the world u - pon my shoulder.
Em                        D      G
   Through the clouds I see love shine
                C            |Em
It keeps me warm as life grows colder.
```

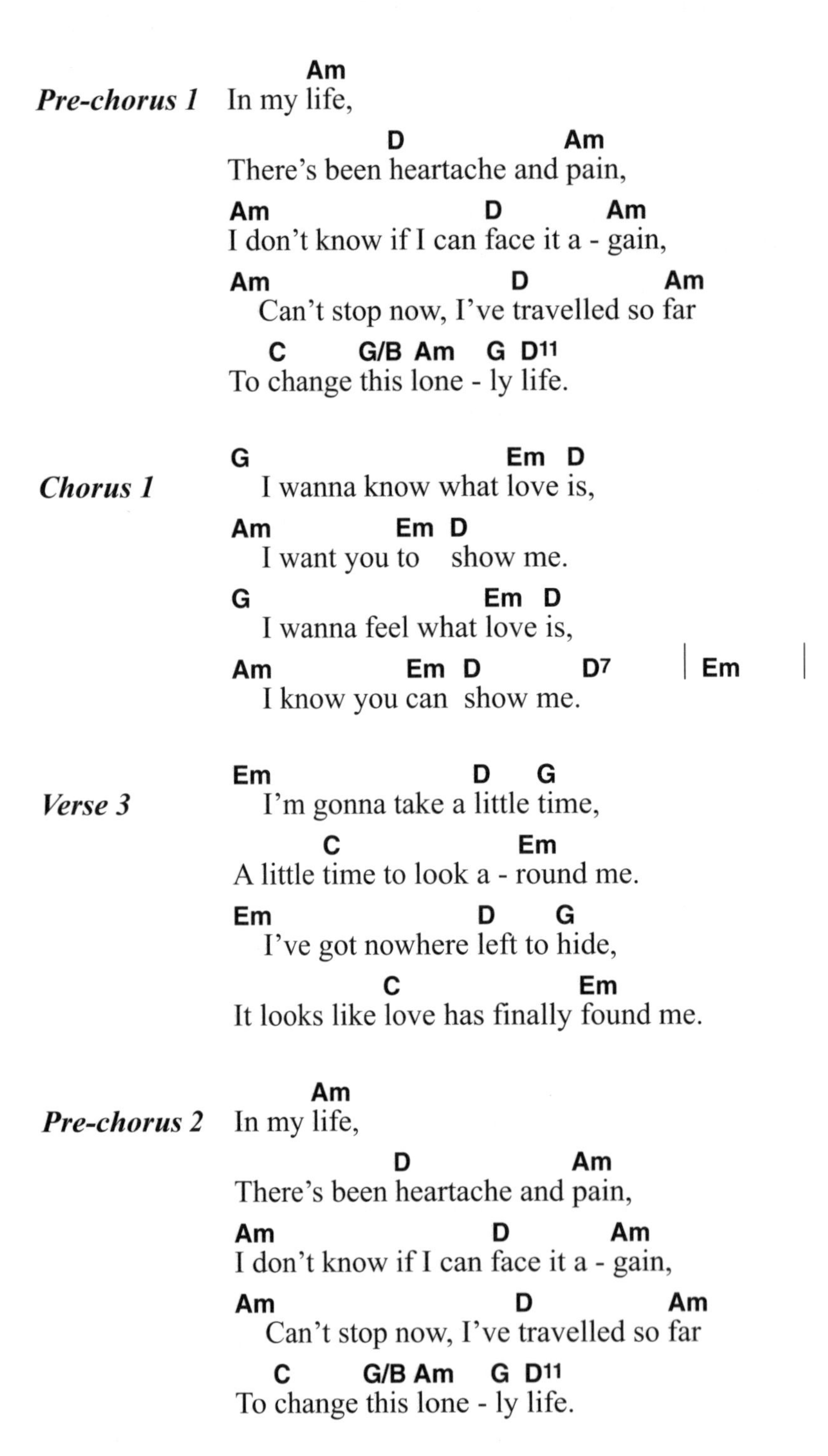

Pre-chorus 1

Am
In my life,

D Am
There's been heartache and pain,

Am D Am
I don't know if I can face it a - gain,

Am D Am
Can't stop now, I've travelled so far

C G/B Am G D11
To change this lone - ly life.

Chorus 1

G Em D
I wanna know what love is,

Am Em D
I want you to show me.

G Em D
I wanna feel what love is,

Am Em D D7 | Em |
I know you can show me.

Verse 3

Em D G
I'm gonna take a little time,

C Em
A little time to look a - round me.

Em D G
I've got nowhere left to hide,

C Em
It looks like love has finally found me.

Pre-chorus 2

Am
In my life,

D Am
There's been heartache and pain,

Am D Am
I don't know if I can face it a - gain,

Am D Am
Can't stop now, I've travelled so far

C G/B Am G D11
To change this lone - ly life.

Chorus 2

```
G                          Em  D
   I wanna know what love is,
Am              Em  D
   I want you to    show me.
G                        Em  D
   I wanna feel what love is,
Am                Em  D
   I know you can  show me.
G                          Em  D
   I wanna know what love is,
Am                  Em    D
   I want you to show me.
G                        Em  D
   I wanna feel what love is,
Am               Em D         | D
   I know you can show me.
```

Chorus 3

```
                    G     Em   D
Let's talk about love__
                          Am      Em  D
Love that you feel in - side__
                              G     Em   D
And I'm feeling so much love__
                       Am        Em  D | D        |
No, you just can - not hide.
G                          Em  D                         Am
   I wanna know what love is, (let's talk about          love)
              Em  D                        G
I want you to     show me (I wanna feel)
                       Em  D
I wanna feel what love is, (I wanna feel it too)
       Am            Em D
And I know you can show me.
```

To fade

Walk This Way

Words & Music by
Joe Perry & Steven Tyler

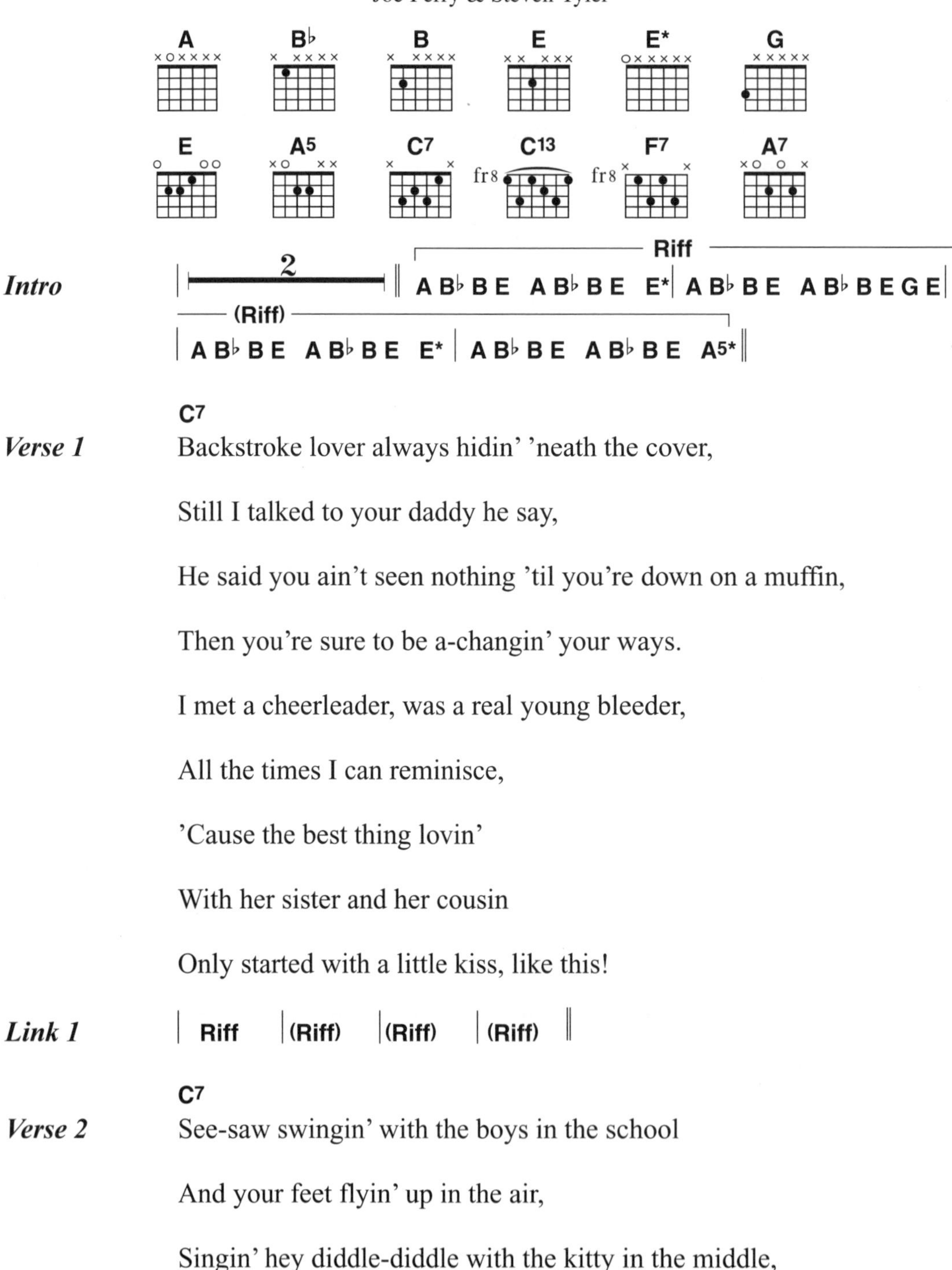

Intro | 2 || A B♭ B E A B♭ B E E* | A B♭ B E A B♭ B E G E |
Riff
| A B♭ B E A B♭ B E E* | A B♭ B E A B♭ B E A5* ||
(Riff)

Verse 1
C7
Backstroke lover always hidin' 'neath the cover,

Still I talked to your daddy he say,

He said you ain't seen nothing 'til you're down on a muffin,

Then you're sure to be a-changin' your ways.

I met a cheerleader, was a real young bleeder,

All the times I can reminisce,

'Cause the best thing lovin'

With her sister and her cousin

Only started with a little kiss, like this!

Link 1 | Riff | (Riff) | (Riff) | (Riff) ||

Verse 2
C7
See-saw swingin' with the boys in the school

And your feet flyin' up in the air,

Singin' hey diddle-diddle with the kitty in the middle,

You be swingin' like you just didn't care.

cont. So I took a big chance at the high school dance

With a missy who was ready to play

Was it me she was foolin'

'Cause she knew what she was doin'

And I know love was here to stay

When she told me to

C13 F7

Chorus 1 Walk this way, walk this way
C13 F7
Walk this way, walk this way
C13 F7
Walk this way, walk this way
C13 F7
Walk this way, walk this way
C7 | C7 | C7 | C7
Ah, just give me a kiss
A5
- like this!

Link 2 | Riff | (Riff) | (Riff) | (Riff) ||

C7

Verse 3 School girl Sadie with the classy, kinda sassy,

Little skirt climbing way up her knees,

There was three young ladies in the school gym locker

When I noticed they was lookin' at me.

I was a high school loser

Never made it with a lady

Till the boys told me something I missed,

Then my next door neighbour

cont. With a daughter had a favour,

C7
So I gave her just a little kiss, like this!

Link 3 | **Riff** | **(Riff)** | **(Riff)** | **(Riff)** ||

C7
Verse 4 See-saw swingin' with the boys in the school

And your feet flyin' up in the air ,

Singin' hey diddle-diddle with the kitty in the middle,

You be swingin' like you just didn't care.

So I took a big chance at the high school dance

With a missy who was ready to play.

Was it me she was foolin',

'Cause she knew what she was doin',

When she told me how to walk this way.

She told me to

C13 F7
Chorus 2 Walk this way, walk this way,
C13 F7
Walk this way, walk this way,
C13 F7
Walk this way, walk this way ,
C13 F7
Walk this way, walk this way,
C7 | C7 | C7 | C7
Ah, just give me a kiss
A5
\- like this!

Outro |: **Riff** | **(Riff)** | **(Riff)** | **(Riff)** :| *Repeat to fade*
(Guitar solo)

The Boys Are Back In Town

Words & Music by
Phil Lynott

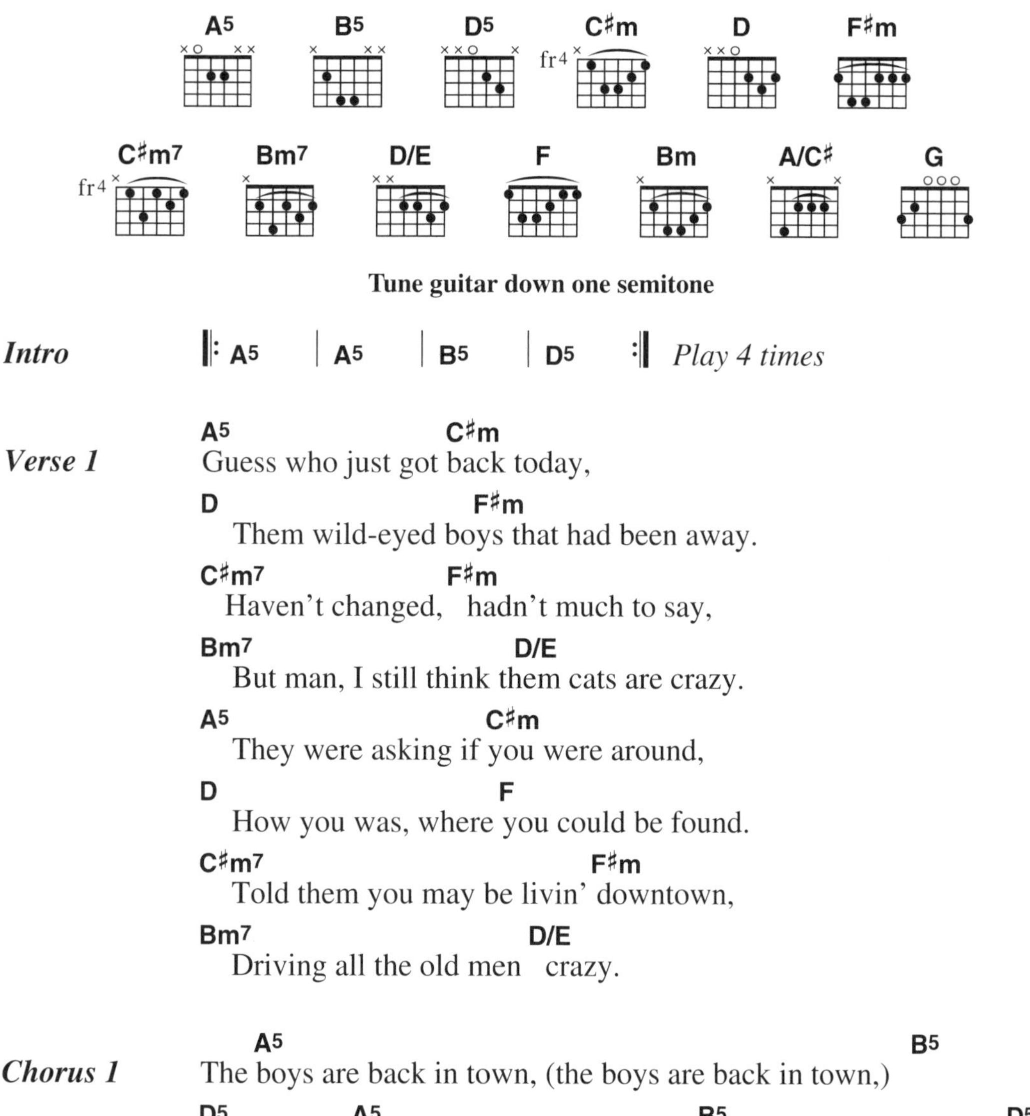

Tune guitar down one semitone

Intro ‖: A5 | A5 | B5 | D5 :‖ *Play 4 times*

Verse 1

```
A5                   C♯m
Guess who just got back today,
D                      F♯m
   Them wild-eyed boys that had been away.
C♯m7                  F♯m
  Haven't changed,   hadn't much to say,
Bm7                          D/E
   But man, I still think them cats are crazy.
A5                           C♯m
   They were asking if you were around,
D                          F
   How you was, where you could be found.
C♯m7                                  F♯m
   Told them you may be livin' downtown,
Bm7                            D/E
   Driving all the old men   crazy.
```

Chorus 1

```
    A5                                                  B5
The boys are back in town, (the boys are back in town,)
D5           A5                          B5                      D5
   I said the boys are back in town, (the boys are back in town,)
    A5
The boys are back in town, (the boys are back in town,)
B5                   D5
The boys are back in town, (the boys are back.)
```

Instrumental ‖: A5 | Bm | A/C♯ | D/E :‖

Verse 2

A5 C♯m
You know that chick that used to dance a lot?
D F♯m
Every night she'd be on the floor shakin' what she got.
C♯m7 F♯m
Man, when I tell you she was cool, she was red hot,
Bm7 D/E
I mean... steaming!
A5 C♯m
And that time over at Johnny's place,
D F
Well, this chick got up and she slapped Johnny's face.
C♯m7 F♯m
Man we fell about the place,
Bm7 D/E
If that chick don't wanna know, forget her.

Chorus 2

A5 B5
The boys are back in town, (the boys are back in town,)
D5 A5 B5 D5
I said the boys are back in town, (the boys are back in town,)
A5
The boys are back in town, (the boys are back in town,)
B5 D5
The boys are back in town, (the boys are back.)

Instrumental ‖: A5 | Bm | A/C♯ | D/E :‖

‖: G | D | C♯m7 | F♯m | Bm7 | D/E | F♯m | F♯m :‖

Verse 3

A5 C♯m
Friday night dressed to kill,
D F♯m
Down at Dino's bar and grill.
C♯m7 F♯m
The drink will flow and blood will spill
Bm7 D/E
And if the boys wanna fight you better let 'em.

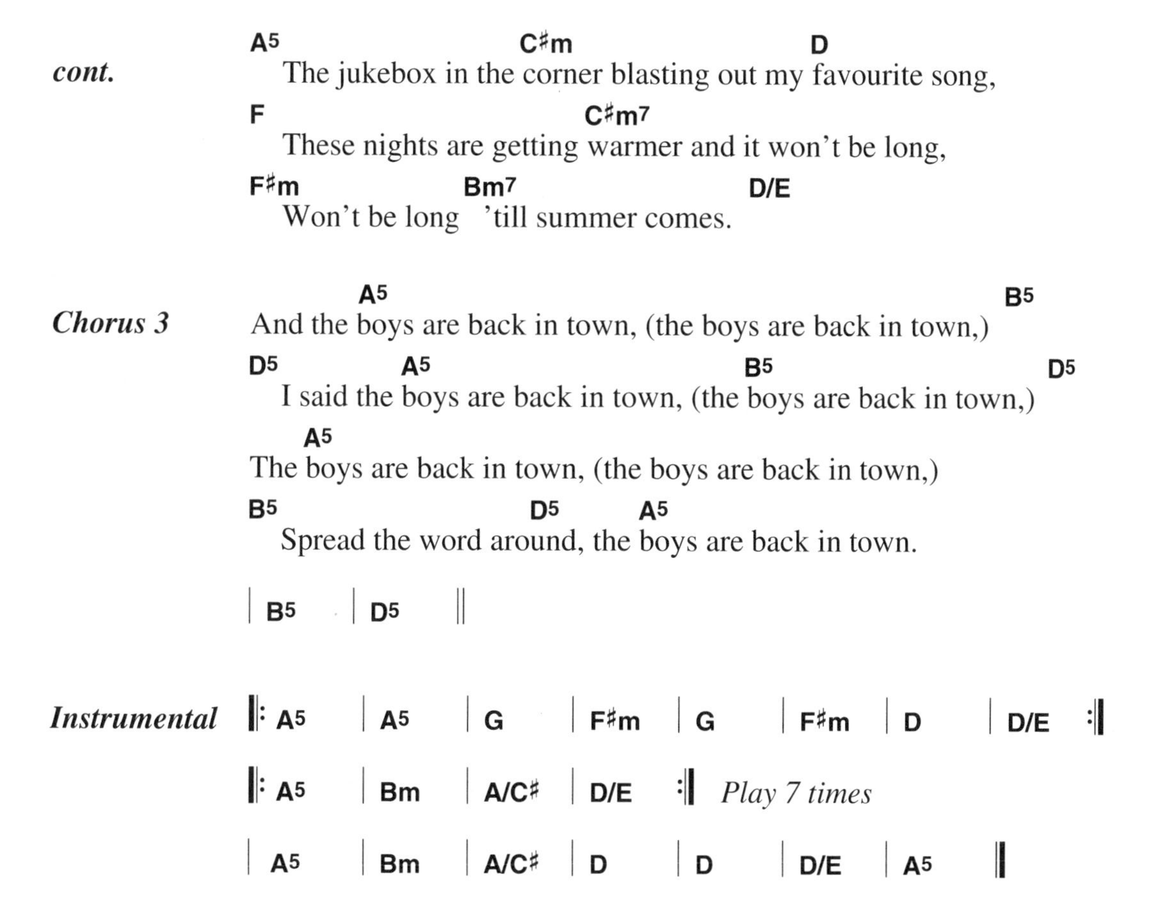

cont.

A5 C♯m D
The jukebox in the corner blasting out my favourite song,

F C♯m7
These nights are getting warmer and it won't be long,

F♯m Bm7 D/E
Won't be long 'till summer comes.

Chorus 3

A5 B5
And the boys are back in town, (the boys are back in town,)

D5 A5 B5 D5
I said the boys are back in town, (the boys are back in town,)

A5
The boys are back in town, (the boys are back in town,)

B5 D5 A5
Spread the word around, the boys are back in town.

| B5 | D5 ||

Instrumental

||: A5 | A5 | G | F♯m | G | F♯m | D | D/E :||

||: A5 | Bm | A/C♯ | D/E :|| *Play 7 times*

| A5 | Bm | A/C♯ | D | D | D/E | A5 ||

School's Out

Words & Music by
Alice Cooper, Michael Bruce, Dennis Dunaway, Neal Smith & Glen Buxton

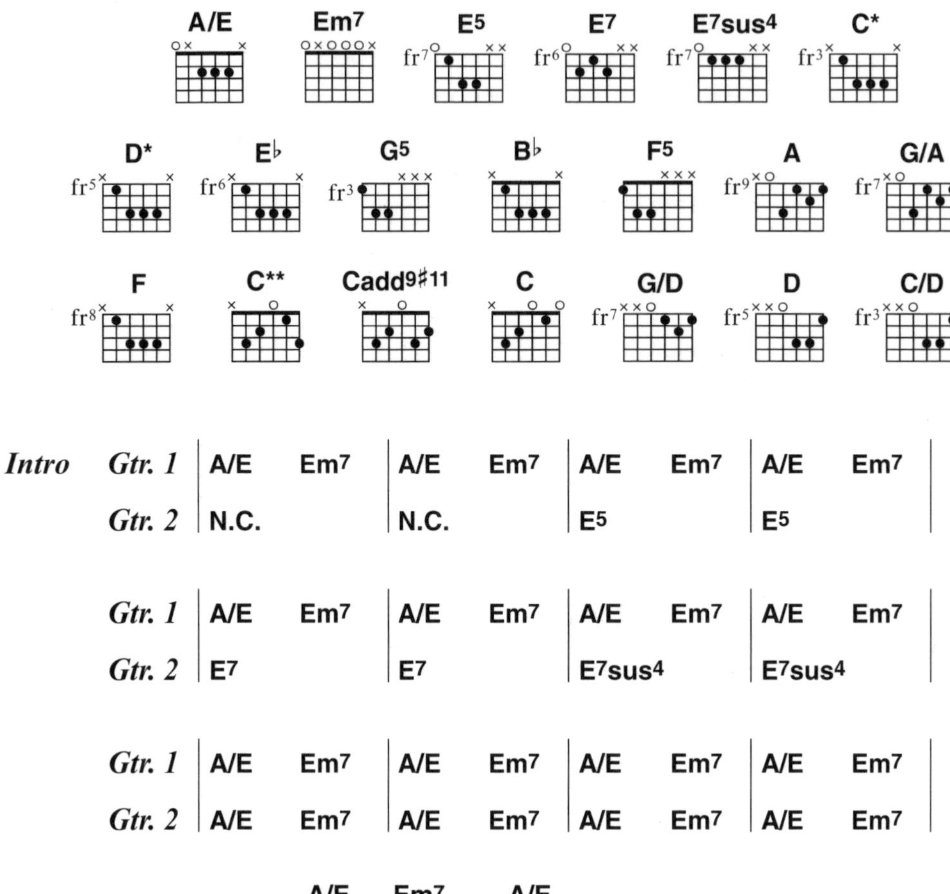

Intro

Gtr. 1	A/E Em7	A/E Em7	A/E Em7	A/E Em7
Gtr. 2	N.C.	N.C.	E5	E5
Gtr. 1	A/E Em7	A/E Em7	A/E Em7	A/E Em7
Gtr. 2	E7	E7	E7sus4	E7sus4
Gtr. 1	A/E Em7	A/E Em7	A/E Em7	A/E Em7
Gtr. 2	A/E Em7	A/E Em7	A/E Em7	A/E Em7

Verse 1

```
                A/E    Em7     A/E
Well we got no choice,
Em7           A/E        Em7  A/E
   All the girls and boys
Em7          A/E      Em7  A/E
   Making all that noise
Em7                 A/E          Em7    A/E
   'Cause they found new toys.
Em7          C*
   Well we can't salute ya,
                        D*
Can't find a flag,
E♭
If that don't suit ya

That's a drag.
```

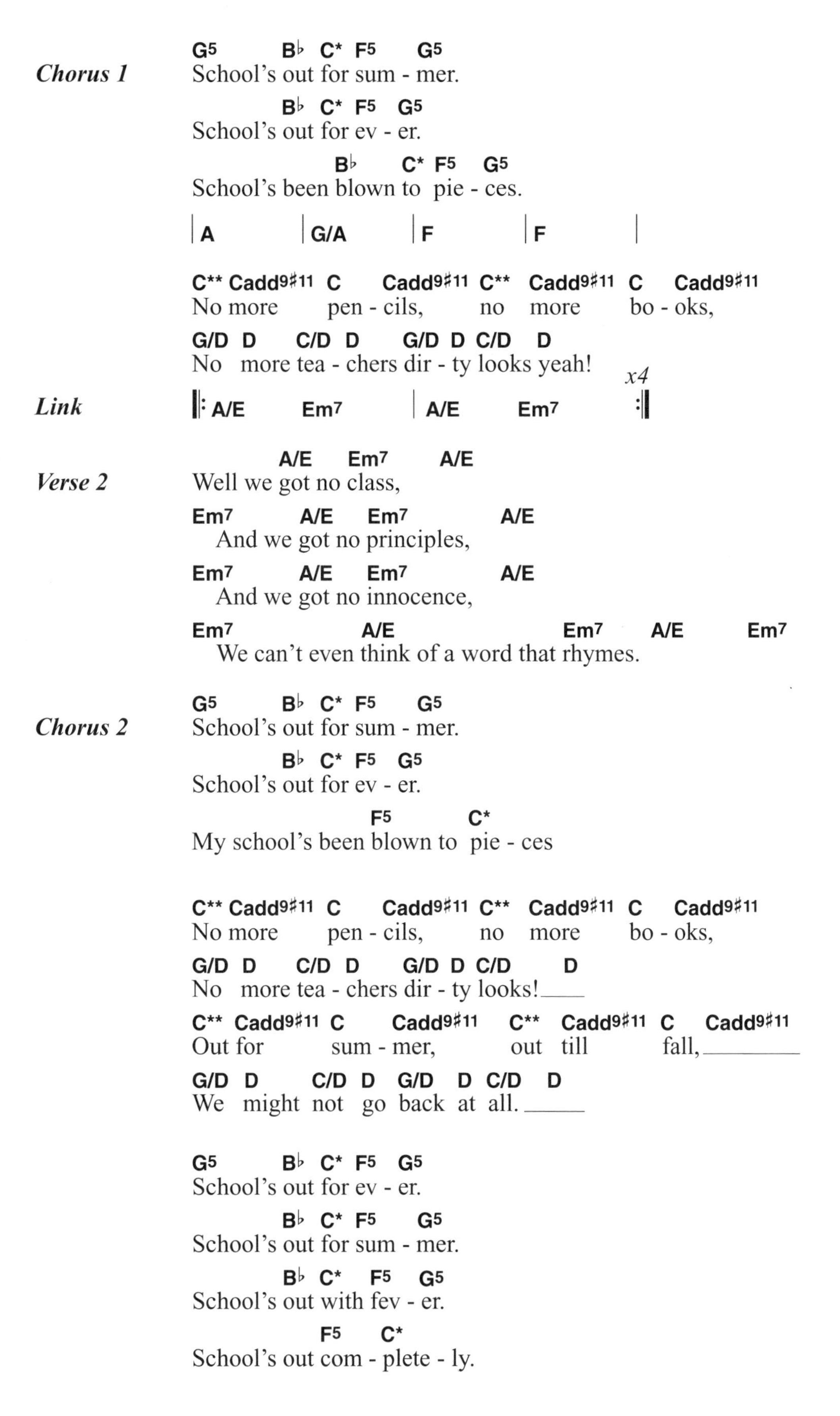
Chorus 1
G5 B♭ C* F5 G5
School's out for sum - mer.
B♭ C* F5 G5
School's out for ev - er.
B♭ C* F5 G5
School's been blown to pie - ces.
| A | G/A | F | F |
C** Cadd9♯11 C Cadd9♯11 C** Cadd9♯11 C Cadd9♯11
No more pen - cils, no more bo - oks,
G/D D C/D D G/D D C/D D
No more tea - chers dir - ty looks yeah!
Link
x4
|: A/E Em7 | A/E Em7 :|
Verse 2
A/E Em7 A/E
Well we got no class,
Em7 A/E Em7 A/E
And we got no principles,
Em7 A/E Em7 A/E
And we got no innocence,
Em7 A/E Em7 A/E Em7
We can't even think of a word that rhymes.
Chorus 2
G5 B♭ C* F5 G5
School's out for sum - mer.
B♭ C* F5 G5
School's out for ev - er.
F5 C*
My school's been blown to pie - ces
C** Cadd9♯11 C Cadd9♯11 C** Cadd9♯11 C Cadd9♯11
No more pen - cils, no more bo - oks,
G/D D C/D D G/D D C/D D
No more tea - chers dir - ty looks!
C** Cadd9♯11 C Cadd9♯11 C** Cadd9♯11 C Cadd9♯11
Out for sum - mer, out till fall,
G/D D C/D D G/D D C/D D
We might not go back at all.
G5 B♭ C* F5 G5
School's out for ev - er.
B♭ C* F5 G5
School's out for sum - mer.
B♭ C* F5 G5
School's out with fev - er.
F5 C*
School's out com - plete - ly.

Wonderwall

Words & Music by
Noel Gallagher

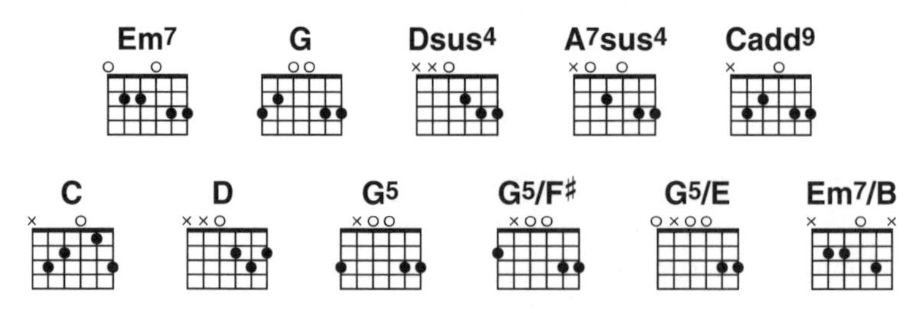

Capo second fret

Intro ‖: Em7 G | Dsus4 | A7sus4 | Em7 G | Dsus4 | A7sus4 :‖

Verse 1

Em7 G
Today is gonna be the day
Dsus4 A7sus4
That they're gonna throw it back to you,
Em7 G
By now you should have somehow
Dsus4 A7sus4
Realised what you gotta do.
Em7 G Dsus4 A7sus4
I don't believe that anybody feels the way I do
Cadd9 Dsus4 | A7sus4 ‖
About you now.

Verse 2

Em7 G
Back beat, the word is on the street
Dsus4 A7sus4
That the fire in your heart is out,
Em7 G
I'm sure you've heard it all before,
Dsus4 A7sus4
But you never really had a doubt.
Em7 G Dsus4 A7sus4
I don't believe that anybody feels the way I do
Em7 G | Dsus4 A7sus4 ‖
About you now.

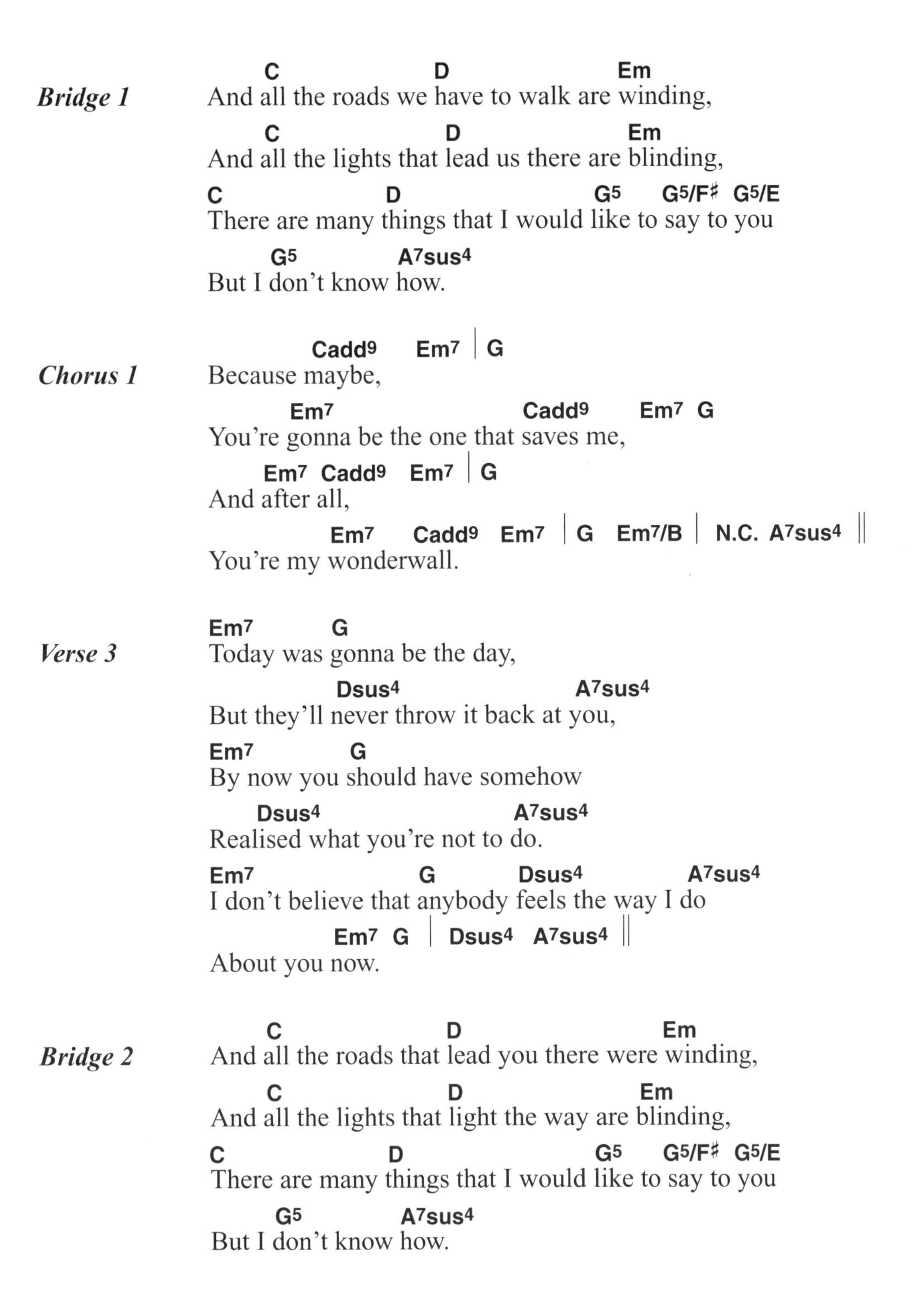

Bridge 1

C D Em
And all the roads we have to walk are winding,

C D Em
And all the lights that lead us there are blinding,

C D G5 G5/F♯ G5/E
There are many things that I would like to say to you

G5 A7sus4
But I don't know how.

Chorus 1

Cadd9 Em7 | G
Because maybe,

Em7 Cadd9 Em7 G
You're gonna be the one that saves me,

Em7 Cadd9 Em7 | G
And after all,

Em7 Cadd9 Em7 | G Em7/B | N.C. A7sus4 ||
You're my wonderwall.

Verse 3

Em7 G
Today was gonna be the day,

Dsus4 A7sus4
But they'll never throw it back at you,

Em7 G
By now you should have somehow

Dsus4 A7sus4
Realised what you're not to do.

Em7 G Dsus4 A7sus4
I don't believe that anybody feels the way I do

Em7 G | Dsus4 A7sus4 ||
About you now.

Bridge 2

C D Em
And all the roads that lead you there were winding,

C D Em
And all the lights that light the way are blinding,

C D G5 G5/F♯ G5/E
There are many things that I would like to say to you

G5 A7sus4
But I don't know how.

Chorus 2

Cadd9 Em7 | G
I said maybe

Em7 Cadd9 Em7 | G
You're gonna be the one that saves me

Em7 Cadd9 Em7 | G
And after all

Em7 Cadd9 Em7 | G Em7 ||
You're my wonderwall.

Chorus 3

As Chorus 2

Outro

Cadd9 Em7 | G
I said maybe

Em7 Cadd9 Em7 | G
You're gonna be the one that saves me,

Em7 Cadd9 Em7 | G
You're gonna be the one that saves me,

Em7 Cadd9 Em7 | G Em7 ||
You're gonna be the one that saves me.

Instrumental ||: Cadd9 Em7 | G Em7 | Cadd9 Em7 | G Em7 :||

Bat Out Of Hell

Words & Music by
Jim Steinman

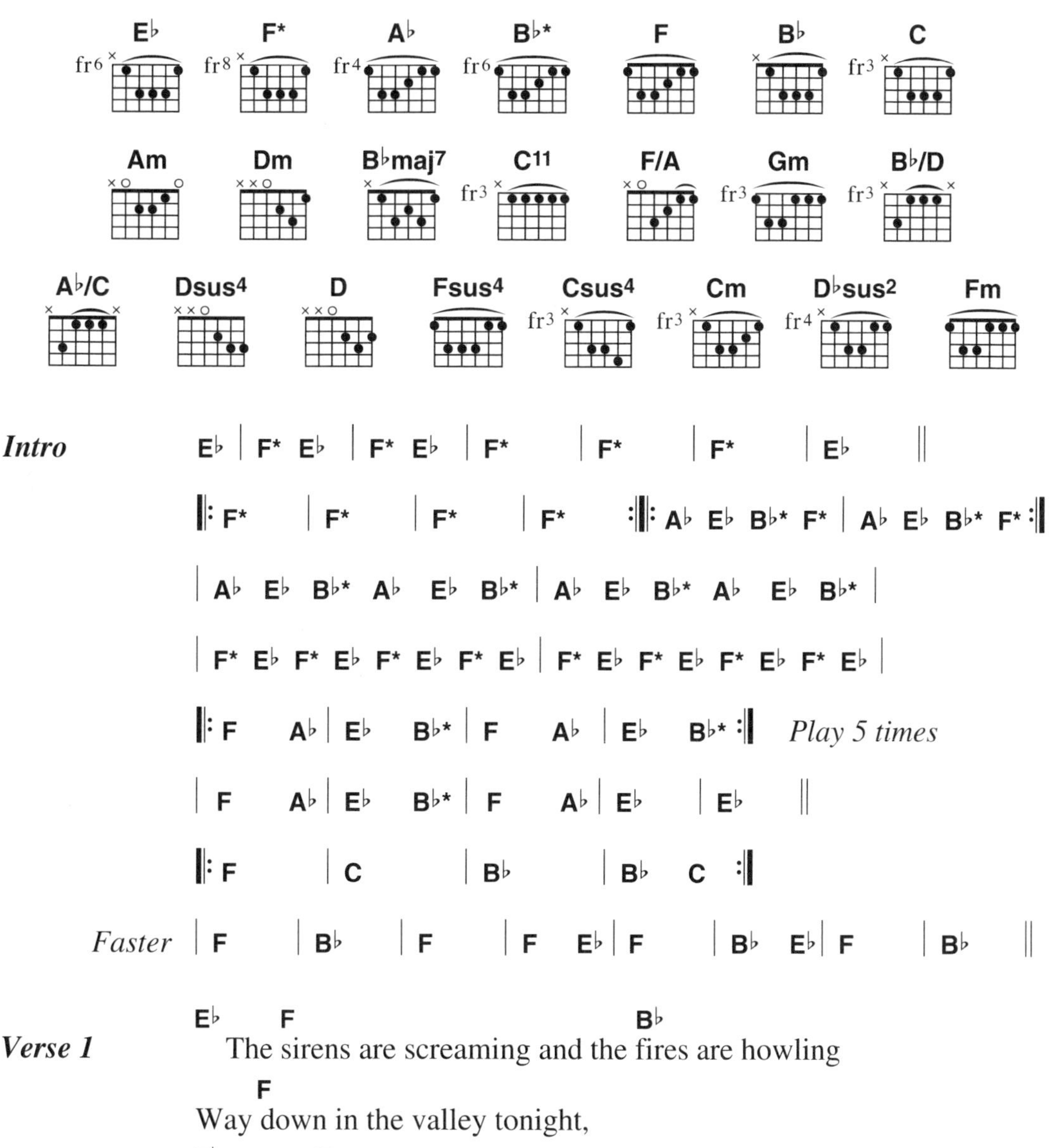

Verse 1

```
E♭    F                             B♭
   The sirens are screaming and the fires are howling
      F
Way down in the valley tonight,
E♭          F                            Am
There's a man in the shadows with a gun in his eye
          B♭
And a blade shining oh so bright,
            F                           C
There's evil in the air and there's thunder in the sky
          Dm                  C    B♭
And a killer's on the bloodshot streets,
```

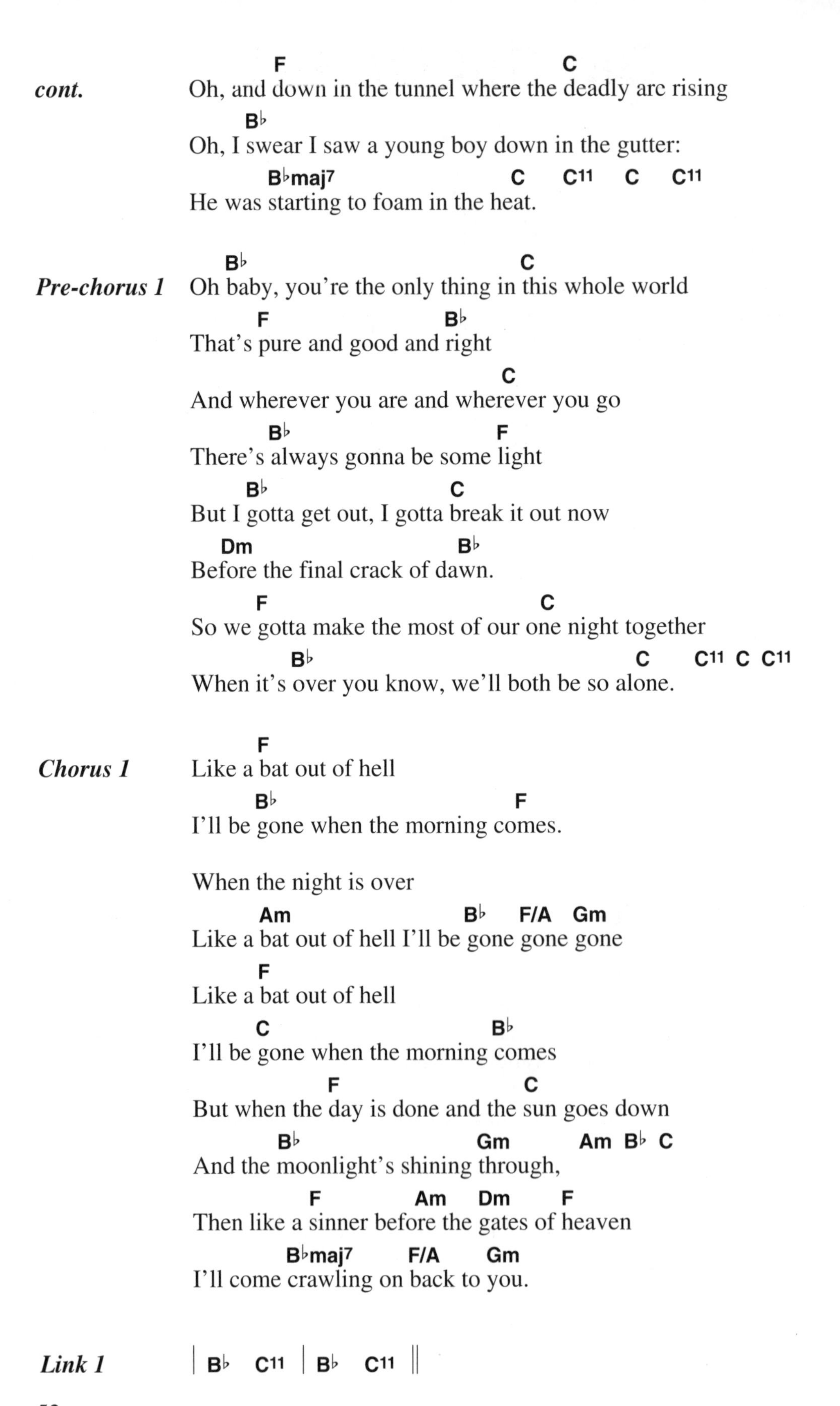

cont.

F C
Oh, and down in the tunnel where the deadly arc rising
B♭
Oh, I swear I saw a young boy down in the gutter:
B♭maj7 C C11 C C11
He was starting to foam in the heat.

Pre-chorus 1

B♭ C
Oh baby, you're the only thing in this whole world
F B♭
That's pure and good and right
C
And wherever you are and wherever you go
B♭ F
There's always gonna be some light
B♭ C
But I gotta get out, I gotta break it out now
Dm B♭
Before the final crack of dawn.
F C
So we gotta make the most of our one night together
B♭ C C11 C C11
When it's over you know, we'll both be so alone.

Chorus 1

F
Like a bat out of hell
B♭ F
I'll be gone when the morning comes.

When the night is over
Am B♭ F/A Gm
Like a bat out of hell I'll be gone gone gone
F
Like a bat out of hell
C B♭
I'll be gone when the morning comes
F C
But when the day is done and the sun goes down
B♭ Gm Am B♭ C
And the moonlight's shining through,
F Am Dm F
Then like a sinner before the gates of heaven
B♭maj7 F/A Gm
I'll come crawling on back to you.

Link 1

| B♭ C11 | B♭ C11 ||

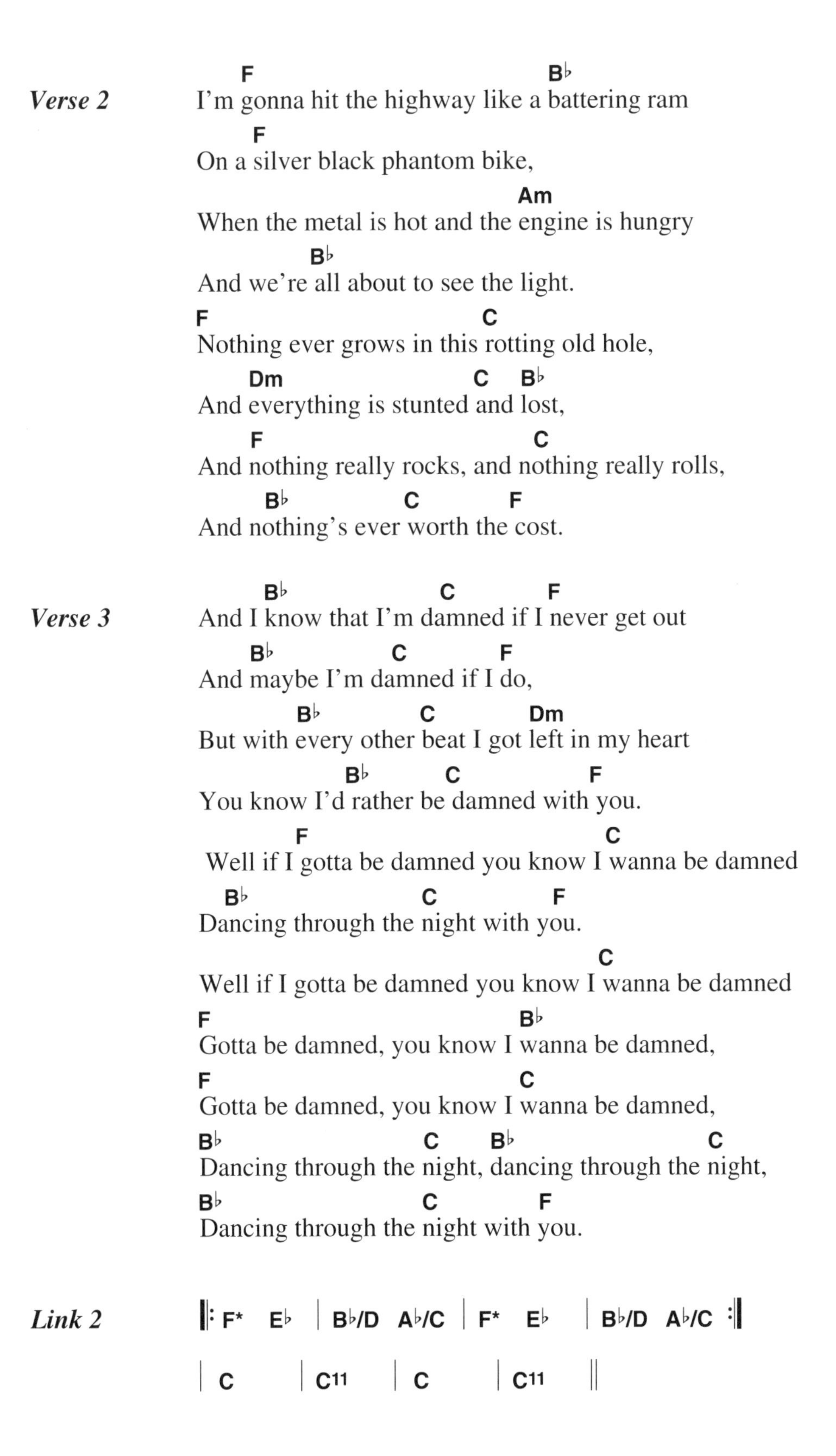

Verse 2

F Bb
I'm gonna hit the highway like a battering ram
F
On a silver black phantom bike,
Am
When the metal is hot and the engine is hungry
Bb
And we're all about to see the light.
F C
Nothing ever grows in this rotting old hole,
Dm C Bb
And everything is stunted and lost,
F C
And nothing really rocks, and nothing really rolls,
Bb C F
And nothing's ever worth the cost.

Verse 3

Bb C F
And I know that I'm damned if I never get out
Bb C F
And maybe I'm damned if I do,
Bb C Dm
But with every other beat I got left in my heart
Bb C F
You know I'd rather be damned with you.
F C
Well if I gotta be damned you know I wanna be damned
Bb C F
Dancing through the night with you.
C
Well if I gotta be damned you know I wanna be damned
F Bb
Gotta be damned, you know I wanna be damned,
F C
Gotta be damned, you know I wanna be damned,
Bb C Bb C
Dancing through the night, dancing through the night,
Bb C F
Dancing through the night with you.

Link 2

‖: F* Eb | Bb/D Ab/C | F* Eb | Bb/D Ab/C :‖

| C | C11 | C | C11 ‖

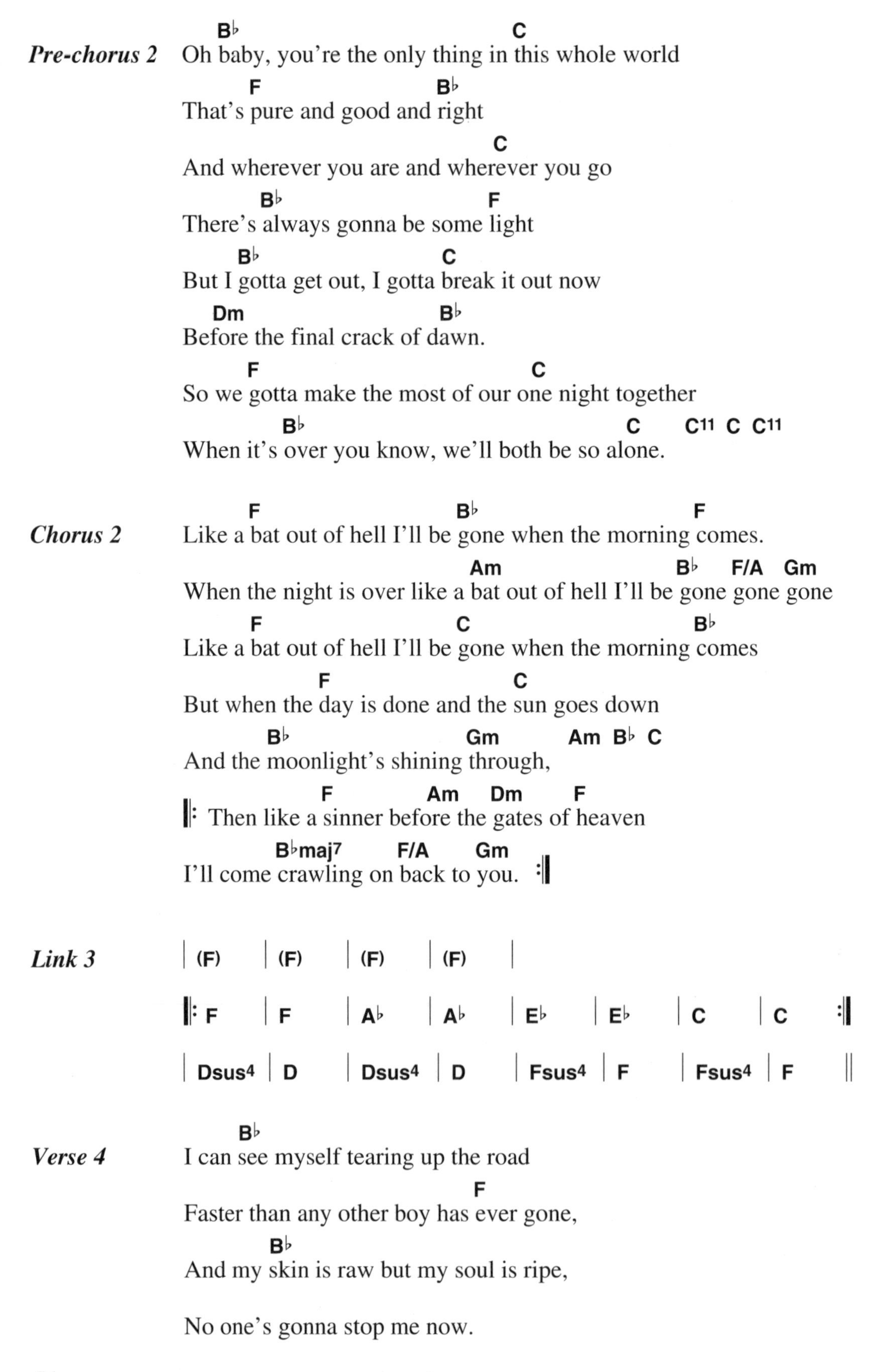

Pre-chorus 2

B♭ C
Oh baby, you're the only thing in this whole world
F B♭
That's pure and good and right
C
And wherever you are and wherever you go
B♭ F
There's always gonna be some light
B♭ C
But I gotta get out, I gotta break it out now
Dm B♭
Before the final crack of dawn.
F C
So we gotta make the most of our one night together
B♭ C C11 C C11
When it's over you know, we'll both be so alone.

Chorus 2

F B♭ F
Like a bat out of hell I'll be gone when the morning comes.
Am B♭ F/A Gm
When the night is over like a bat out of hell I'll be gone gone gone
F C B♭
Like a bat out of hell I'll be gone when the morning comes
F C
But when the day is done and the sun goes down
B♭ Gm Am B♭ C
And the moonlight's shining through,
F Am Dm F
𝄆 Then like a sinner before the gates of heaven
B♭maj7 F/A Gm
I'll come crawling on back to you. 𝄇

Link 3

| (F) | (F) | (F) | (F) |

𝄆 F | F | A♭ | A♭ | E♭ | E♭ | C | C 𝄇

| Dsus4 | D | Dsus4 | D | Fsus4 | F | Fsus4 | F ||

Verse 4

B♭
I can see myself tearing up the road
F
Faster than any other boy has ever gone,
B♭
And my skin is raw but my soul is ripe,

No one's gonna stop me now.

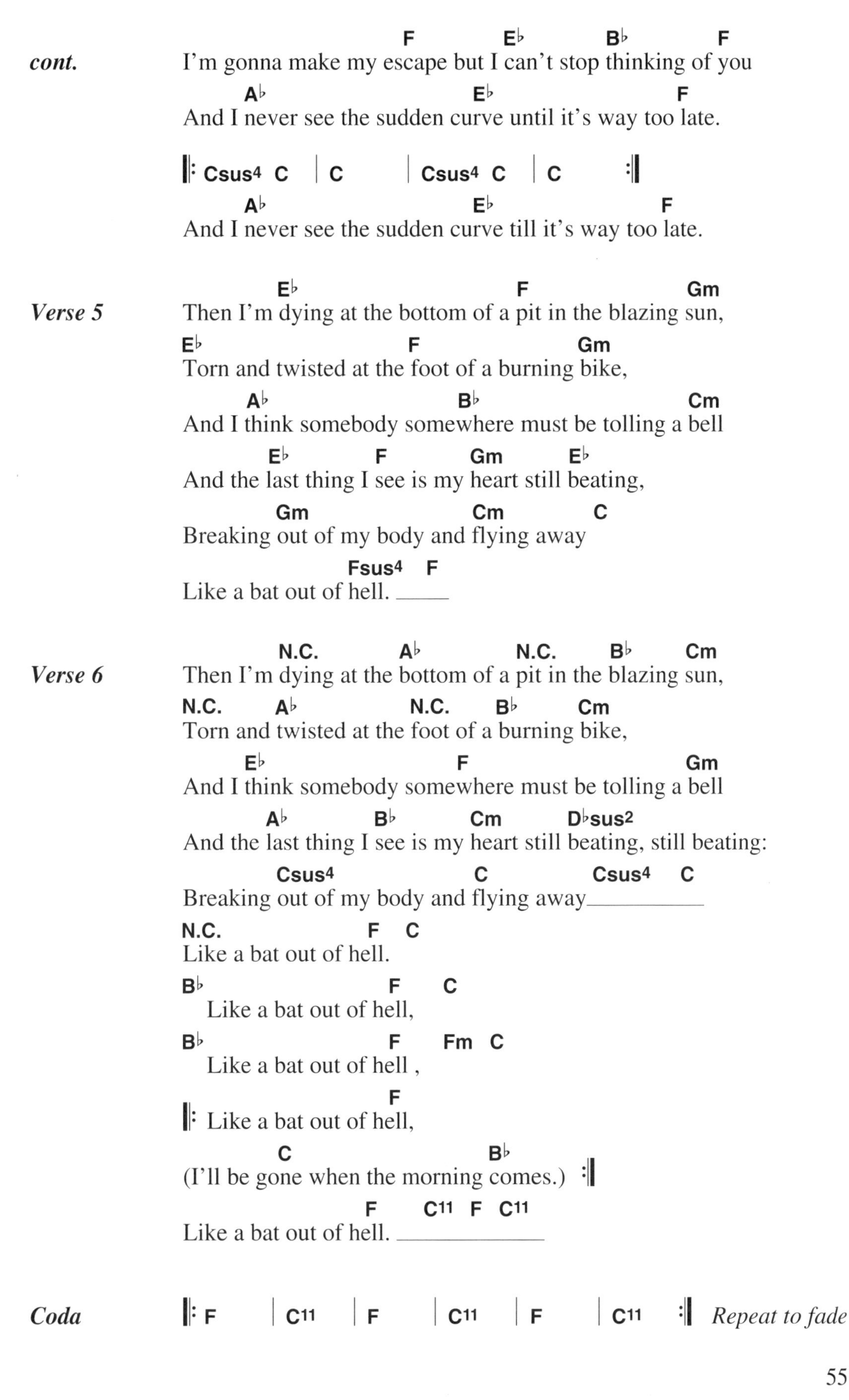

cont.

F E♭ B♭ F
I'm gonna make my escape but I can't stop thinking of you
A♭ E♭ F
And I never see the sudden curve until it's way too late.

‖: Csus4 C | C | Csus4 C | C :‖

A♭ E♭ F
And I never see the sudden curve till it's way too late.

Verse 5

E♭ F Gm
Then I'm dying at the bottom of a pit in the blazing sun,
E♭ F Gm
Torn and twisted at the foot of a burning bike,
A♭ B♭ Cm
And I think somebody somewhere must be tolling a bell
E♭ F Gm E♭
And the last thing I see is my heart still beating,
Gm Cm C
Breaking out of my body and flying away
Fsus4 F
Like a bat out of hell. _____

Verse 6

N.C. A♭ N.C. B♭ Cm
Then I'm dying at the bottom of a pit in the blazing sun,
N.C. A♭ N.C. B♭ Cm
Torn and twisted at the foot of a burning bike,
E♭ F Gm
And I think somebody somewhere must be tolling a bell
A♭ B♭ Cm D♭sus2
And the last thing I see is my heart still beating, still beating:
Csus4 C Csus4 C
Breaking out of my body and flying away__________
N.C. F C
Like a bat out of hell.
B♭ F C
Like a bat out of hell,
B♭ F Fm C
Like a bat out of hell ,
F
‖: Like a bat out of hell,
C B♭
(I'll be gone when the morning comes.) :‖
F C11 F C11
Like a bat out of hell. __________

Coda

‖: F | C11 | F | C11 | F | C11 :‖ *Repeat to fade*

Thriller

Words & Music by
Rod Temperton

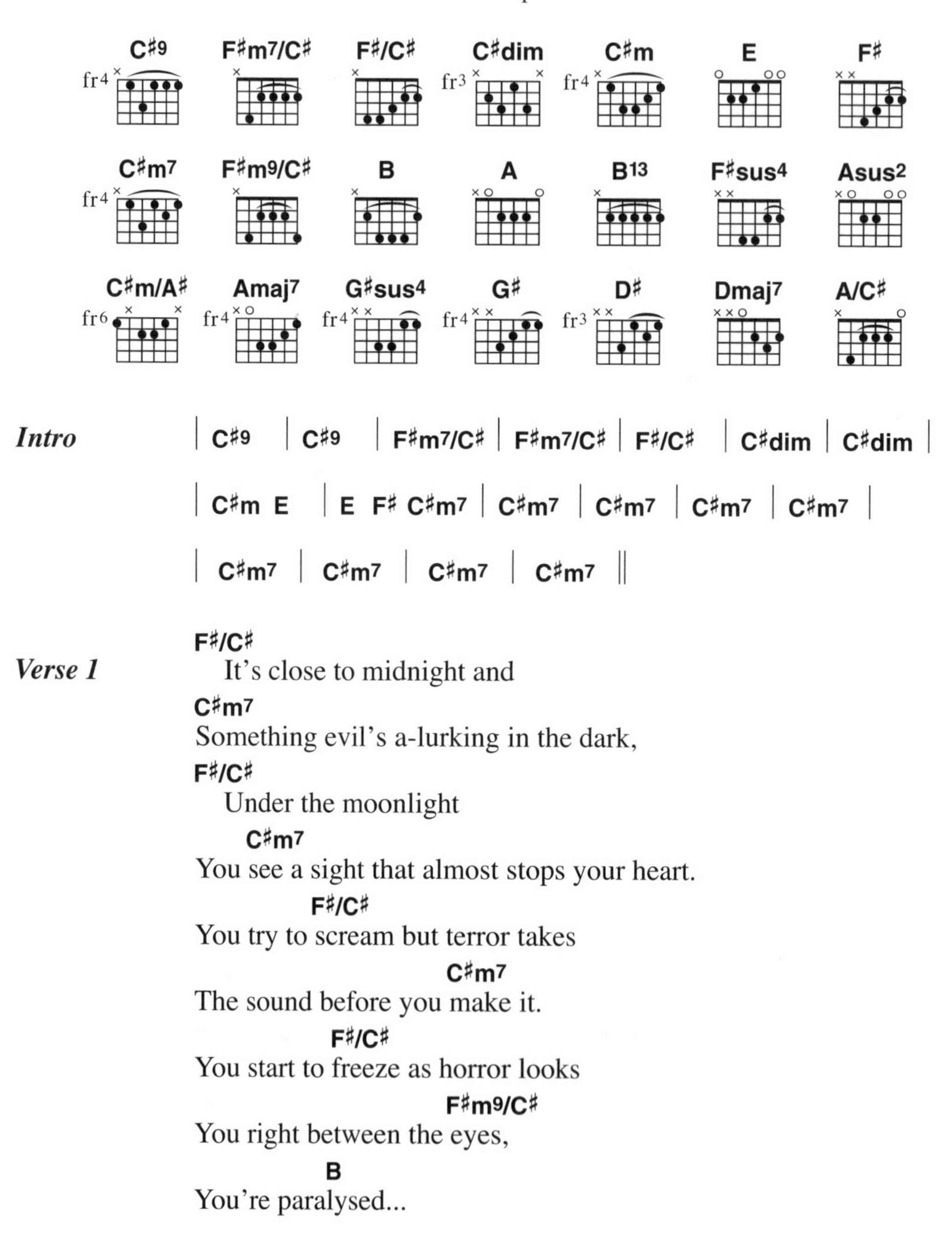

Intro

| C♯9 | C♯9 | F♯m7/C♯ | F♯m7/C♯ | F♯/C♯ | C♯dim | C♯dim |

| C♯m E | E F♯ C♯m7 | C♯m7 | C♯m7 | C♯m7 | C♯m7 |

| C♯m7 | C♯m7 | C♯m7 | C♯m7 ||

Verse 1

F♯/C♯
It's close to midnight and
C♯m7
Something evil's a-lurking in the dark,
F♯/C♯
Under the moonlight
C♯m7
You see a sight that almost stops your heart.
F♯/C♯
You try to scream but terror takes
C♯m7
The sound before you make it.
F♯/C♯
You start to freeze as horror looks
F♯m9/C♯
You right between the eyes,
B
You're paralysed...

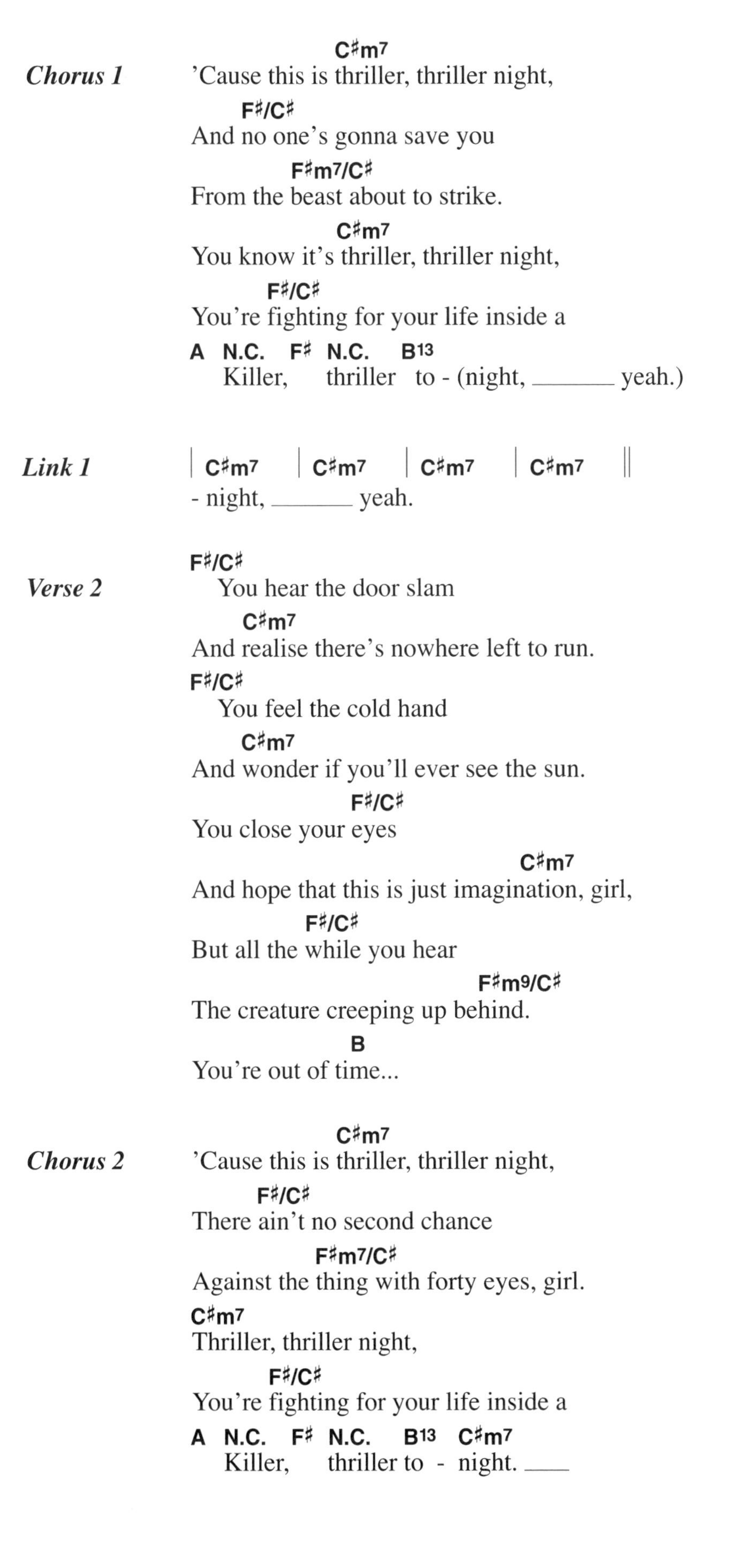

Chorus 1

C♯m7
'Cause this is thriller, thriller night,
F♯/C♯
And no one's gonna save you
F♯m7/C♯
From the beast about to strike.
C♯m7
You know it's thriller, thriller night,
F♯/C♯
You're fighting for your life inside a
A N.C. F♯ N.C. B13
Killer, thriller to - (night, ______ yeah.)

Link 1

| C♯m7 | C♯m7 | C♯m7 | C♯m7 ||
- night, ______ yeah.

Verse 2

F♯/C♯
You hear the door slam
C♯m7
And realise there's nowhere left to run.
F♯/C♯
You feel the cold hand
C♯m7
And wonder if you'll ever see the sun.
F♯/C♯
You close your eyes
C♯m7
And hope that this is just imagination, girl,
F♯/C♯
But all the while you hear
F♯m9/C♯
The creature creeping up behind.
B
You're out of time...

Chorus 2

C♯m7
'Cause this is thriller, thriller night,
F♯/C♯
There ain't no second chance
F♯m7/C♯
Against the thing with forty eyes, girl.
C♯m7
Thriller, thriller night,
F♯/C♯
You're fighting for your life inside a
A N.C. F♯ N.C. B13 C♯m7
Killer, thriller to - night. ____

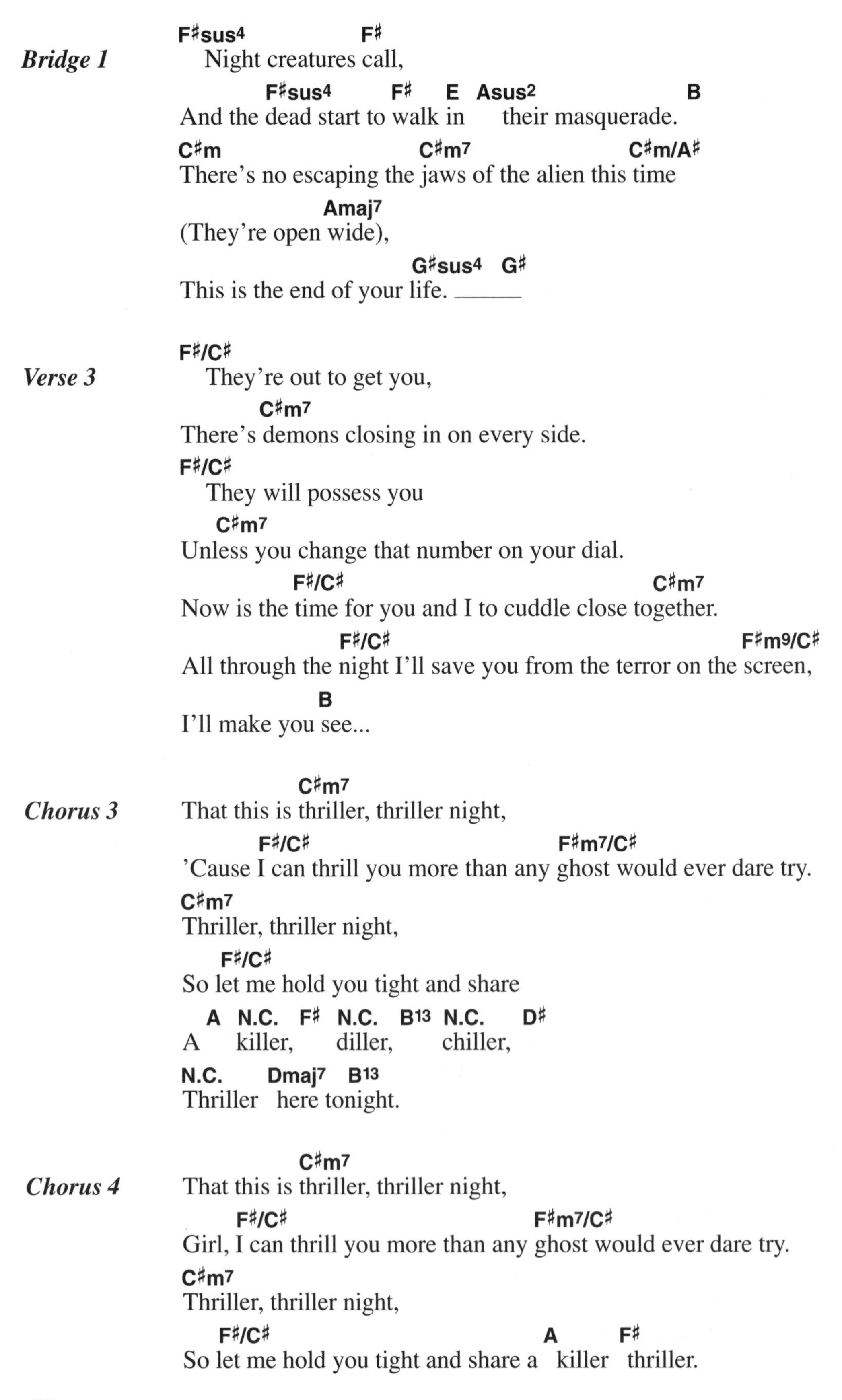

Bridge 1

F#sus4 F#
Night creatures call,

F#sus4 F# E Asus2 B
And the dead start to walk in their masquerade.

C#m C#m7 C#m/A#
There's no escaping the jaws of the alien this time

Amaj7
(They're open wide),

G#sus4 G#
This is the end of your life. ______

Verse 3

F#/C#
They're out to get you,

C#m7
There's demons closing in on every side.

F#/C#
They will possess you

C#m7
Unless you change that number on your dial.

F#/C# C#m7
Now is the time for you and I to cuddle close together.

F#/C# F#m9/C#
All through the night I'll save you from the terror on the screen,

B
I'll make you see...

Chorus 3

C#m7
That this is thriller, thriller night,

F#/C# F#m7/C#
'Cause I can thrill you more than any ghost would ever dare try.

C#m7
Thriller, thriller night,

F#/C#
So let me hold you tight and share

A N.C. F# N.C. B13 N.C. D#
A killer, diller, chiller,

N.C. Dmaj7 B13
Thriller here tonight.

Chorus 4

C#m7
That this is thriller, thriller night,

F#/C# F#m7/C#
Girl, I can thrill you more than any ghost would ever dare try.

C#m7
Thriller, thriller night,

F#/C# A F#
So let me hold you tight and share a killer thriller.

Link 2 | C♯m7 | C♯m7 | C♯m7 | C♯m7 ||

Coda
Spoken

```
C♯m    A/C♯
   Darkness falls across the land,
F♯sus4                  F♯
   The midnight hour   is close at hand.
C♯m                 A/C♯
   Creatures crawl in search of blood
F♯sus4                   F♯
   To terrorise y'awl's neighborhood.
C♯m                          A/C♯
   And whosoever shall be found
             F♯sus4          F♯
Without the soul for getting down
                 C♯m                 A/C♯
Must stand and face the hounds of hell
         F♯sus4            F♯
And rot   inside a corpse's shell.
```

|: C♯m7 | A/C♯ | F♯sus4 | F♯ :|

With vocal ad lib.

```
C♯m  A/C♯           F♯sus4
          The foulest stench is in the air,
     F♯                        C♯m
The funk of forty thousand years,
             A/C♯
And grizzly ghouls from every tomb
F♯sus4              F♯
   Are closing in   to seal your doom.
C♯m                         A/C♯
   And though you fight to   stay alive
F♯sus4                 F♯
   Your body starts to shiver,
  C♯m                        A/C♯
For no mere mortal can resist
     F♯sus4  F♯          C♯m
The evil   of the thriller.
```

Like A Prayer

Words & Music by
Madonna & Pat Leonard

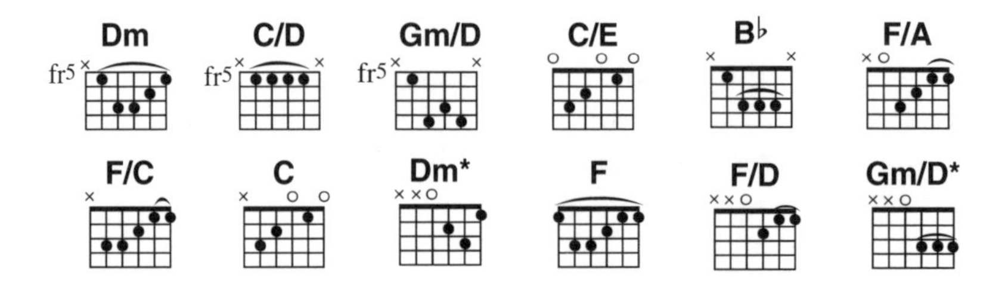

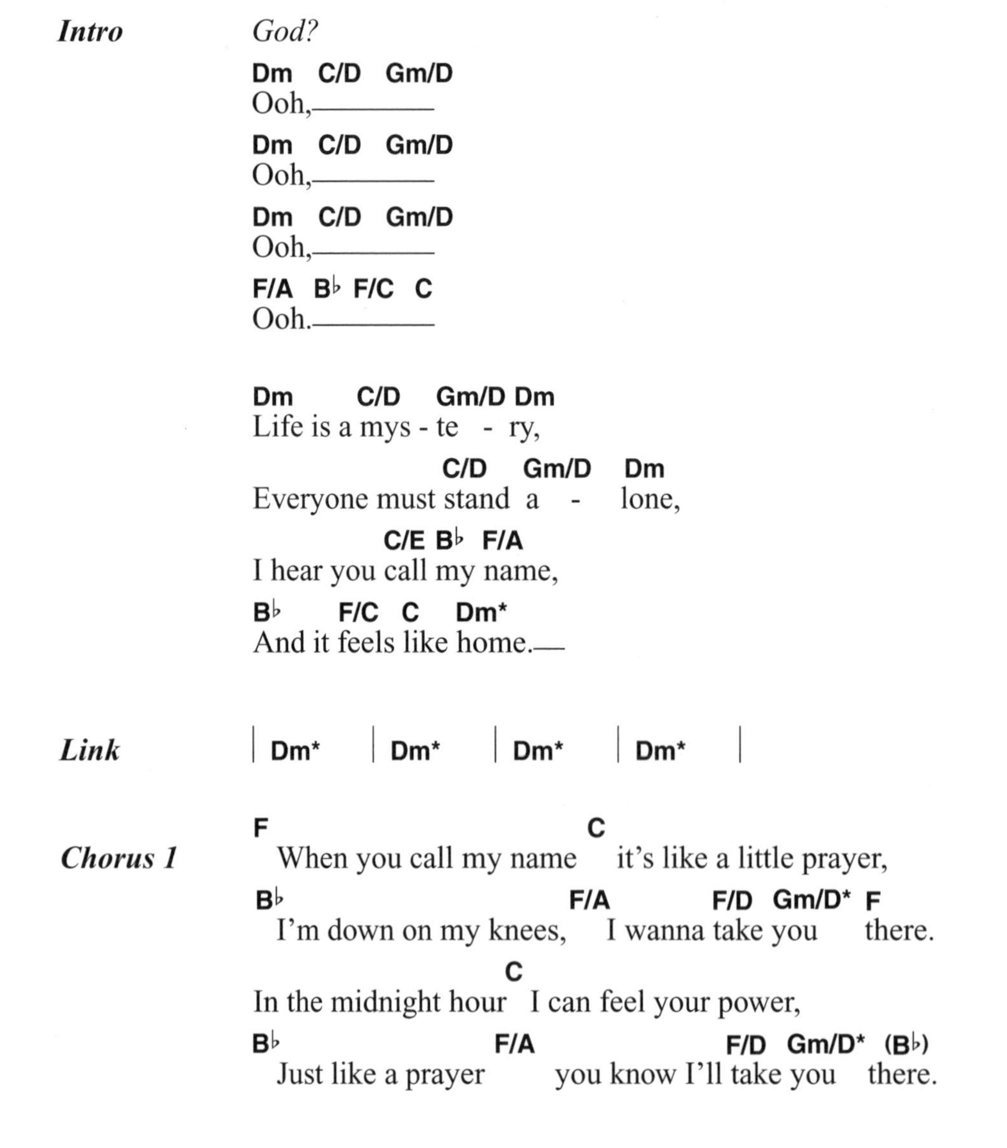

Intro

God?

Dm C/D Gm/D
Ooh,——

Dm C/D Gm/D
Ooh,——

Dm C/D Gm/D
Ooh,——

F/A B♭ F/C C
Ooh.——

Dm C/D Gm/D Dm
Life is a mys - te - ry,

C/D Gm/D Dm
Everyone must stand a - lone,

C/E B♭ F/A
I hear you call my name,

B♭ F/C C Dm*
And it feels like home.—

Link | **Dm*** | **Dm*** | **Dm*** | **Dm*** |

Chorus 1

F C
When you call my name it's like a little prayer,

B♭ F/A F/D Gm/D* F
I'm down on my knees, I wanna take you there.

C
In the midnight hour I can feel your power,

B♭ F/A F/D Gm/D* (B♭)
Just like a prayer you know I'll take you there.

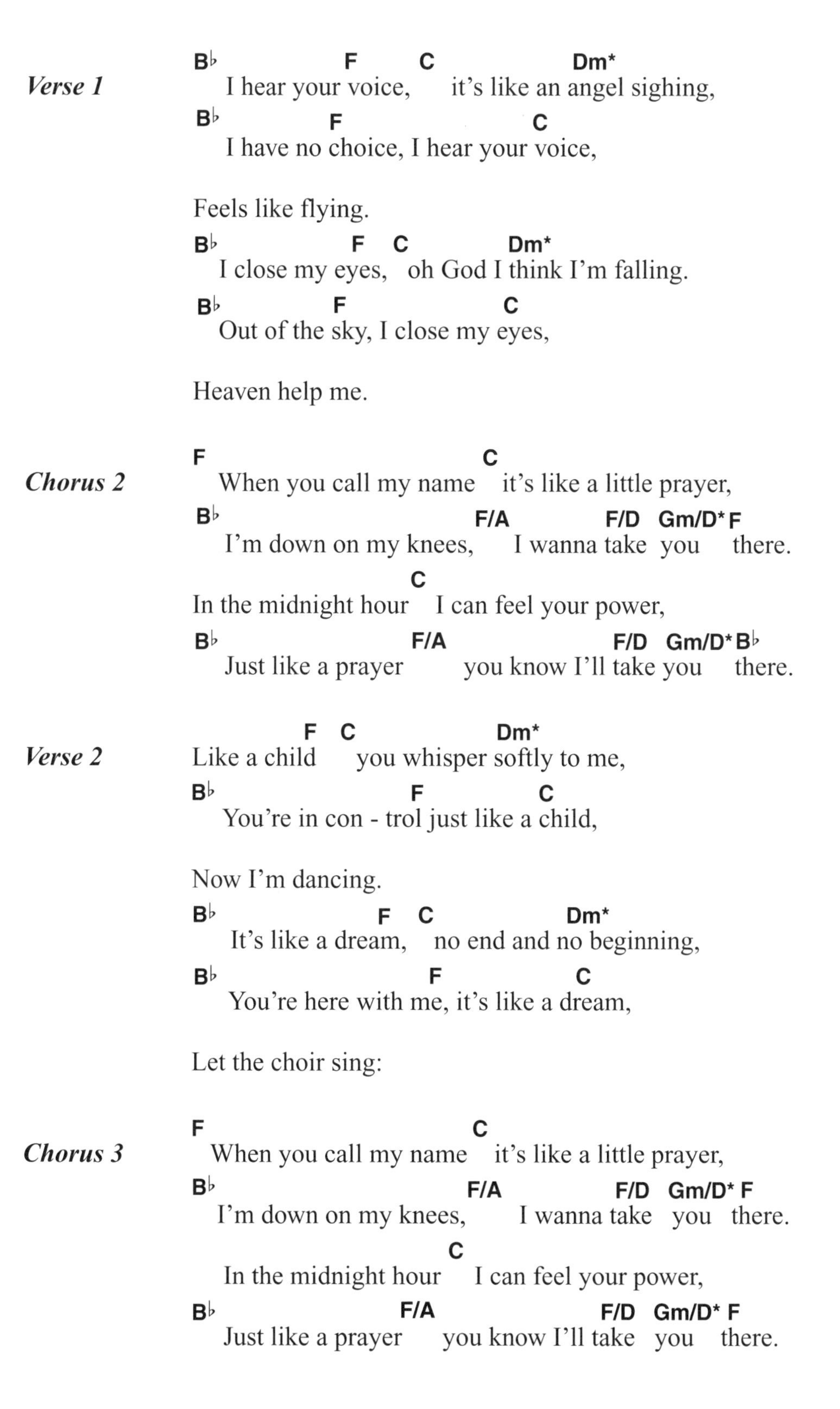

Verse 1

B♭ F C Dm*
I hear your voice, it's like an angel sighing,
B♭ F C
I have no choice, I hear your voice,

Feels like flying.
B♭ F C Dm*
I close my eyes, oh God I think I'm falling.
B♭ F C
Out of the sky, I close my eyes,

Heaven help me.

Chorus 2

F C
When you call my name it's like a little prayer,
B♭ F/A F/D Gm/D* F
I'm down on my knees, I wanna take you there.
C
In the midnight hour I can feel your power,
B♭ F/A F/D Gm/D* B♭
Just like a prayer you know I'll take you there.

Verse 2

F C Dm*
Like a child you whisper softly to me,
B♭ F C
You're in con - trol just like a child,

Now I'm dancing.
B♭ F C Dm*
It's like a dream, no end and no beginning,
B♭ F C
You're here with me, it's like a dream,

Let the choir sing:

Chorus 3

F C
When you call my name it's like a little prayer,
B♭ F/A F/D Gm/D* F
I'm down on my knees, I wanna take you there.
C
In the midnight hour I can feel your power,
B♭ F/A F/D Gm/D* F
Just like a prayer you know I'll take you there.

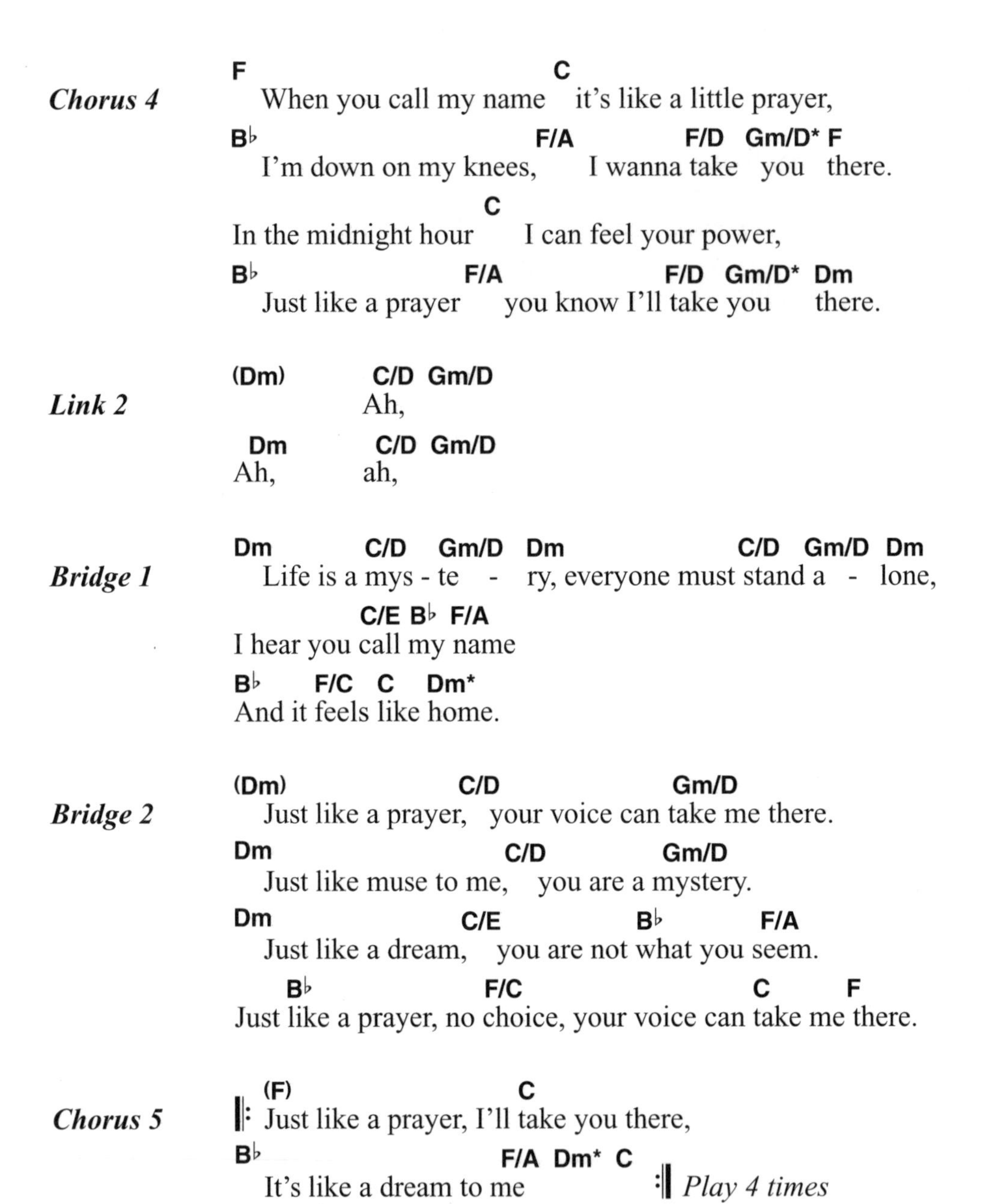

Chorus 4

F C
When you call my name it's like a little prayer,

B♭ F/A F/D Gm/D* F
I'm down on my knees, I wanna take you there.

C
In the midnight hour I can feel your power,

B♭ F/A F/D Gm/D* Dm
Just like a prayer you know I'll take you there.

Link 2

(Dm) C/D Gm/D
Ah,

Dm C/D Gm/D
Ah, ah,

Bridge 1

Dm C/D Gm/D Dm C/D Gm/D Dm
Life is a mys - te - ry, everyone must stand a - lone,

C/E B♭ F/A
I hear you call my name

B♭ F/C C Dm*
And it feels like home.

Bridge 2

(Dm) C/D Gm/D
Just like a prayer, your voice can take me there.

Dm C/D Gm/D
Just like muse to me, you are a mystery.

Dm C/E B♭ F/A
Just like a dream, you are not what you seem.

B♭ F/C C F
Just like a prayer, no choice, your voice can take me there.

Chorus 5

(F) C
𝄆 Just like a prayer, I'll take you there,

B♭ F/A Dm* C
It's like a dream to me 𝄇 *Play 4 times*

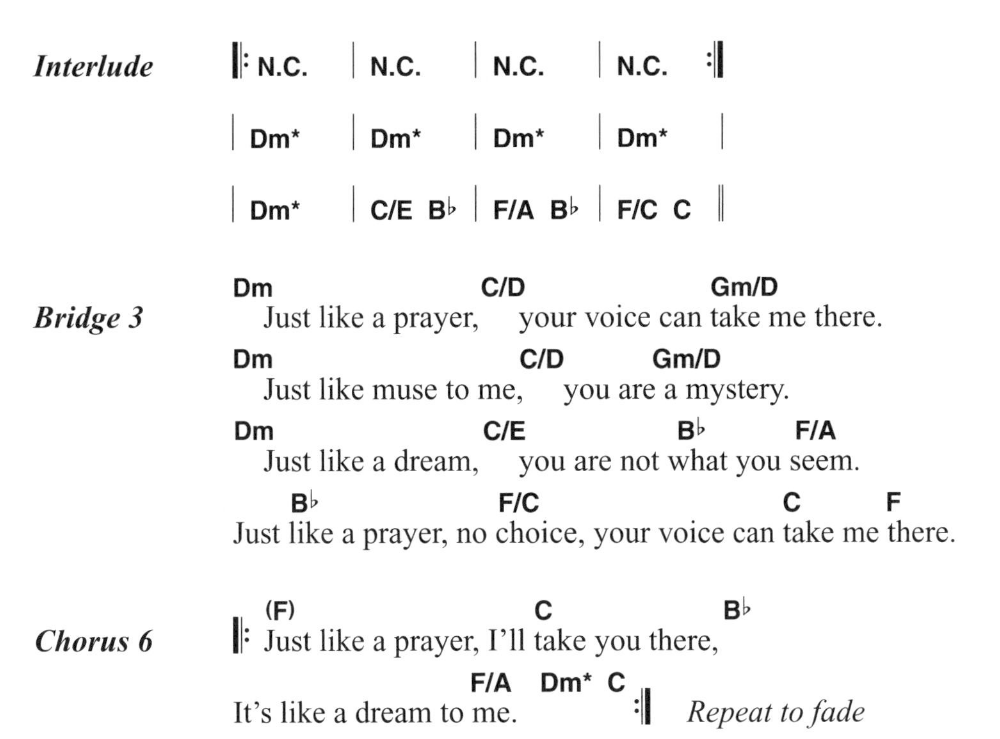
Interlude
N.C. | N.C. | N.C. | N.C.
Dm* | Dm* | Dm* | Dm*
Dm* | C/E B♭ | F/A B♭ | F/C C
Bridge 3
Dm C/D Gm/D
Just like a prayer, your voice can take me there.
Dm C/D Gm/D
Just like muse to me, you are a mystery.
Dm C/E B♭ F/A
Just like a dream, you are not what you seem.
B♭ F/C C F
Just like a prayer, no choice, your voice can take me there.
Chorus 6
(F) C B♭
Just like a prayer, I'll take you there,
F/A Dm* C
It's like a dream to me.
Repeat to fade

Don't Let The Sun Go Down On Me

Words & Music by
Elton John & Bernie Taupin

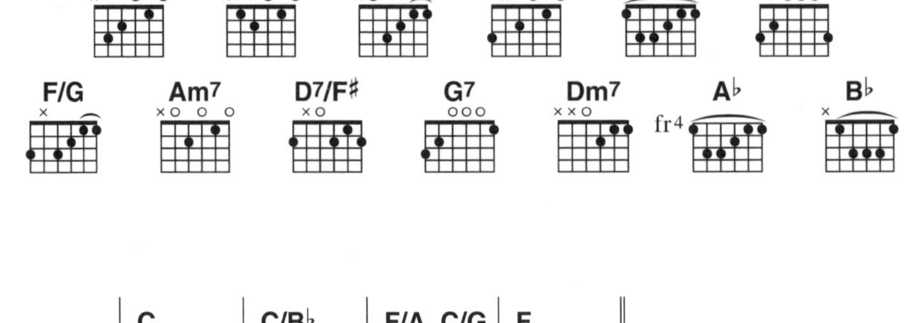

Intro | C | C/B♭ | F/A C/G | F ‖

Verse 1

```
G                                    F      C
  I can't light no more of your   dark - ness,
F                                          G
  All my pictures seem to fade to black and white.
G                                      F    C
  I'm growing tired and time stands still be - fore me,
F                               G
  Frozen here on the ladder of my life.
G                                   F           C
  It's much too late to save myself    from fall - ing,
F                                         G
  I took a chance and changed your way of__ life.
G                                       F       C
  But you misread my meaning when I met you,
F                                  C/G         G        F/G
  Closed the door and left me blinded by the light.
```

Chorus 1

```
C                          C/B♭
  Don't let the sun go down on me, yeah,
Am7                                    D7/F♯
  Although I search myself, it's always someone else I see.
C/G                                  F/G G7           C          C/B♭
  I'd just allow a fragment of your life    to wander free, oh,__
    F/A                            Dm7        C/G   F/G  C
But losing everything is like the sun going down on    me.
```

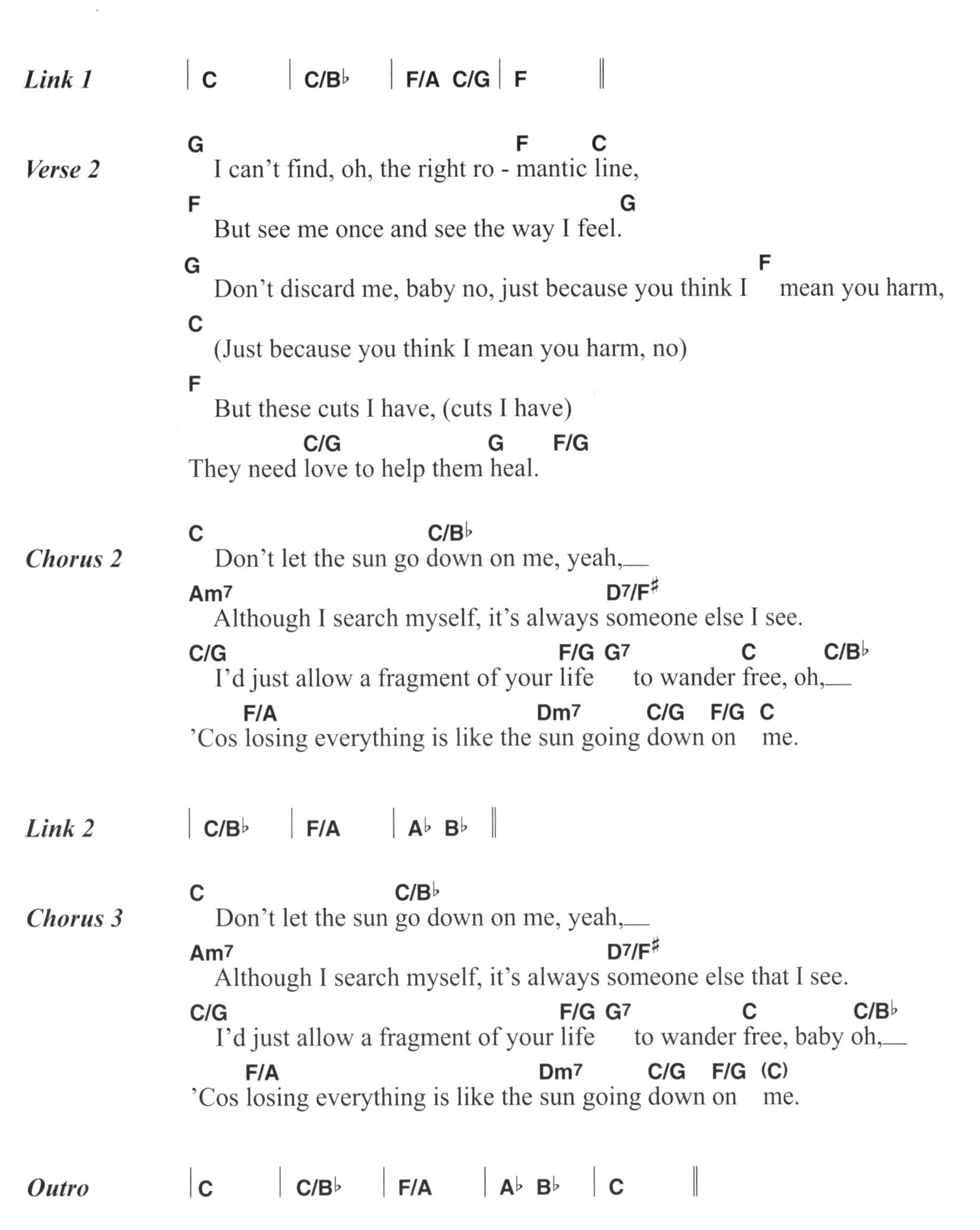

Link 1 | C | C/B♭ | F/A C/G | F ||

Verse 2

G F C
I can't find, oh, the right ro - mantic line,
F G
But see me once and see the way I feel.
G F
Don't discard me, baby no, just because you think I mean you harm,
C
(Just because you think I mean you harm, no)
F
But these cuts I have, (cuts I have)
C/G G F/G
They need love to help them heal.

Chorus 2

C C/B♭
Don't let the sun go down on me, yeah,
Am7 D7/F♯
Although I search myself, it's always someone else I see.
C/G F/G G7 C C/B♭
I'd just allow a fragment of your life to wander free, oh,
F/A Dm7 C/G F/G C
'Cos losing everything is like the sun going down on me.

Link 2 | C/B♭ | F/A | A♭ B♭ ||

Chorus 3

C C/B♭
Don't let the sun go down on me, yeah,
Am7 D7/F♯
Although I search myself, it's always someone else that I see.
C/G F/G G7 C C/B♭
I'd just allow a fragment of your life to wander free, baby oh,
F/A Dm7 C/G F/G (C)
'Cos losing everything is like the sun going down on me.

Outro | C | C/B♭ | F/A | A♭ B♭ | C ||

Saving All My Love For You

Words & Music by
Gerry Goffin & Michael Masser

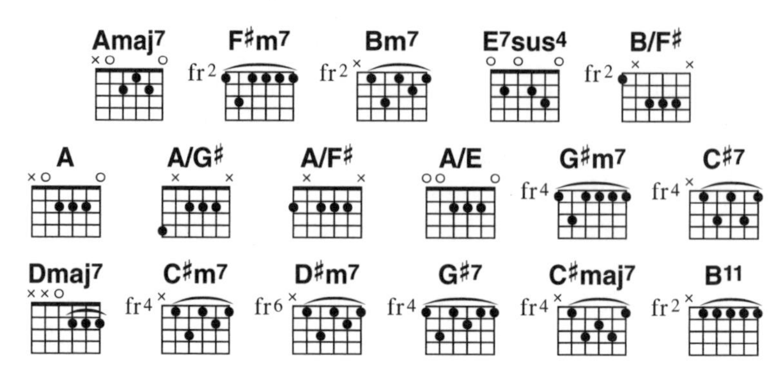

Intro | Amaj7 F#m7 | Bm7 E7sus4 |

| Amaj7 F#m7 | Bm7 E7sus4 ||

Verse 1

```
  Amaj7      F#m7          Bm7         E7sus4
A few stolen moments is all that we share,
Amaj7              F#m7          Bm7              E7sus4
You've got your family, and they need you there,
                F#m7    B/F#           F#m7          B/F#
Though I've tried to resist being last on your list.
    A          A/G#  A/F#  A/E        G#m7    C#7
But no oth - er man's        gonna do,
           Dmaj7  C#m7  Bm7
So I'm saving all my love for you.
```

| Amaj7 F#m7 | Bm7 E7sus4 |

Verse 2

```
     Amaj7     F#m7 Bm7            E7sus4
It's not very easy, living all alone,
     Amaj7           F#m7            Bm7           E7sus4
My friends try and tell me, find a man of my own.
     F#m7           B/F#        F#m7             B/F#
But each time I try, I just break down and cry
          A       A/G#     A/F#   A/E          G#m7    C#7
'Cos I'd rather be         home         feeling blue,
           Dmaj7  C#m7  Bm7      Amaj7
So I'm saving all my love for you.
```

Bridge

G♯m7 C♯7 F♯m7
You used to tell me we'd run away together,

Bm7 E7sus4 A
Love gives you the right to be free.

D♯m7 G♯7 C♯maj7
You said be patient, just wait a little longer,

F♯m7 B11 E7sus4
But that's just an old fanta - sy.

Verse 3

Amaj7 F♯m7 Bm7 E7sus4
I've got to get ready, just a few minutes more,

Amaj7 F♯m7 Bm7 E7sus4
Gonna get that old feeling when you walk through that door.

F♯m7 B/F♯ F♯m7 B/F♯
'Cos to - night is the night for feeling al - right,

A A/G♯ A/F♯ A/E G♯m7 C♯7
We'll be making love the whole night through.

Dmaj7 C♯m7 Bm7
So I'm saving all my love,

Dmaj7 C♯m7 Bm7
Yes, I'm saving all my love,

Dmaj7 C♯m7 Bm7 Amaj7 F♯m7 Bm7 E7sus4
Yes, I'm saving all my love for you.__________

Amaj7 F♯m7 Bm7 E7sus4
No other woman is gonna love you more

F♯m7 B/F♯ F♯m7 B/F♯
'Cos to - night is the night that I'm feeling al - right,

A A/G♯ A/F♯ A/E G♯m7 C♯7
We'll be making love the whole night through.

Dmaj7 C♯m7 Bm7
So I'm saving all my love,

Dmaj7 C♯m7 Bm7
Yeah, I'm saving all my lovin',

Dmaj7 C♯m7 Bm7 Amaj7 F♯m7 Bm7 E7sus4
Yes, I'm saving all my love for you.__________

Amaj7 F♯m7 Bm7 E7sus4
For you,__________

Amaj7 F♯m7 Bm7 E7sus4
For you.__________ *To fade*

Believe

Words & Music by
Brian Higgins, Paul Barry & Steve Torch

G D Am Bm7 Em C Gmaj7 Am7

Tune guitar down a semitone

Intro

| : G | D | Am | Am |

| G | Bm7 | Am | Em : |

| G | D | Am | C |
After love, after love

| G | Bm7 | Am | Em ||

Verse 1

G
No matter how hard I try
Gmaj7
You keep pushing me aside
C
And I can't break through,
D
There's no talking to you.
G
So sad that you're leaving,
Bm7
Takes time to believe it,
C
But after all is said and done
D
You're going to be the lonely one, oh.

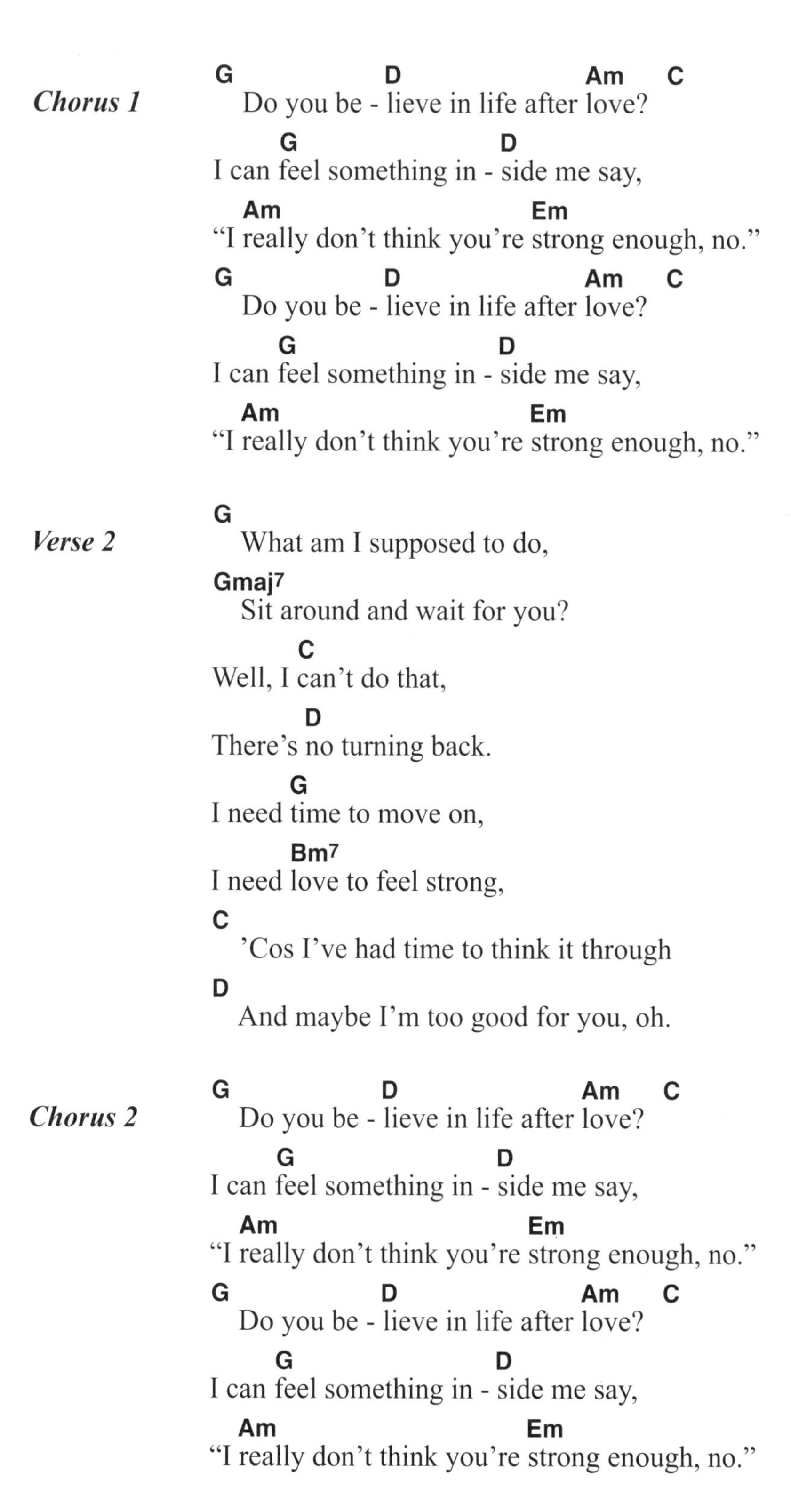

Chorus 1

G D Am C
Do you be - lieve in life after love?
G D
I can feel something in - side me say,
Am Em
"I really don't think you're strong enough, no."
G D Am C
Do you be - lieve in life after love?
G D
I can feel something in - side me say,
Am Em
"I really don't think you're strong enough, no."

Verse 2

G
What am I supposed to do,
Gmaj7
Sit around and wait for you?
C
Well, I can't do that,
D
There's no turning back.
G
I need time to move on,
Bm7
I need love to feel strong,
C
'Cos I've had time to think it through
D
And maybe I'm too good for you, oh.

Chorus 2

G D Am C
Do you be - lieve in life after love?
G D
I can feel something in - side me say,
Am Em
"I really don't think you're strong enough, no."
G D Am C
Do you be - lieve in life after love?
G D
I can feel something in - side me say,
Am Em
"I really don't think you're strong enough, no."

```
            Em                     D
*Bridge*      Well, I know that I'll get through this
            Em                D
              'Cos I know that I am strong,
                    C
            And I don't need you anymore,
                   D
            Oh, I don't need you anymore,
                   C                Am7
            Oh, I don't need you anymore,
                   D
            No, I don't need you anymore.

              G          D               Am   C
Chorus 3    |: Do you be - lieve in life after love?
               G                  Bm7
            I can feel something in - side me say,
              Am                     Em
            "I really don't think you're strong enough, no."
            G          D               Am   C
              Do you be - lieve in life after love?
               G                  D
            I can feel something in - side me say,
              Am                     Em
            "I really don't think you're strong enough, no." :|  Repeat to fade
```

You Win Again

Words & Music by
Barry Gibb, Maurice Gibb & Robin Gibb

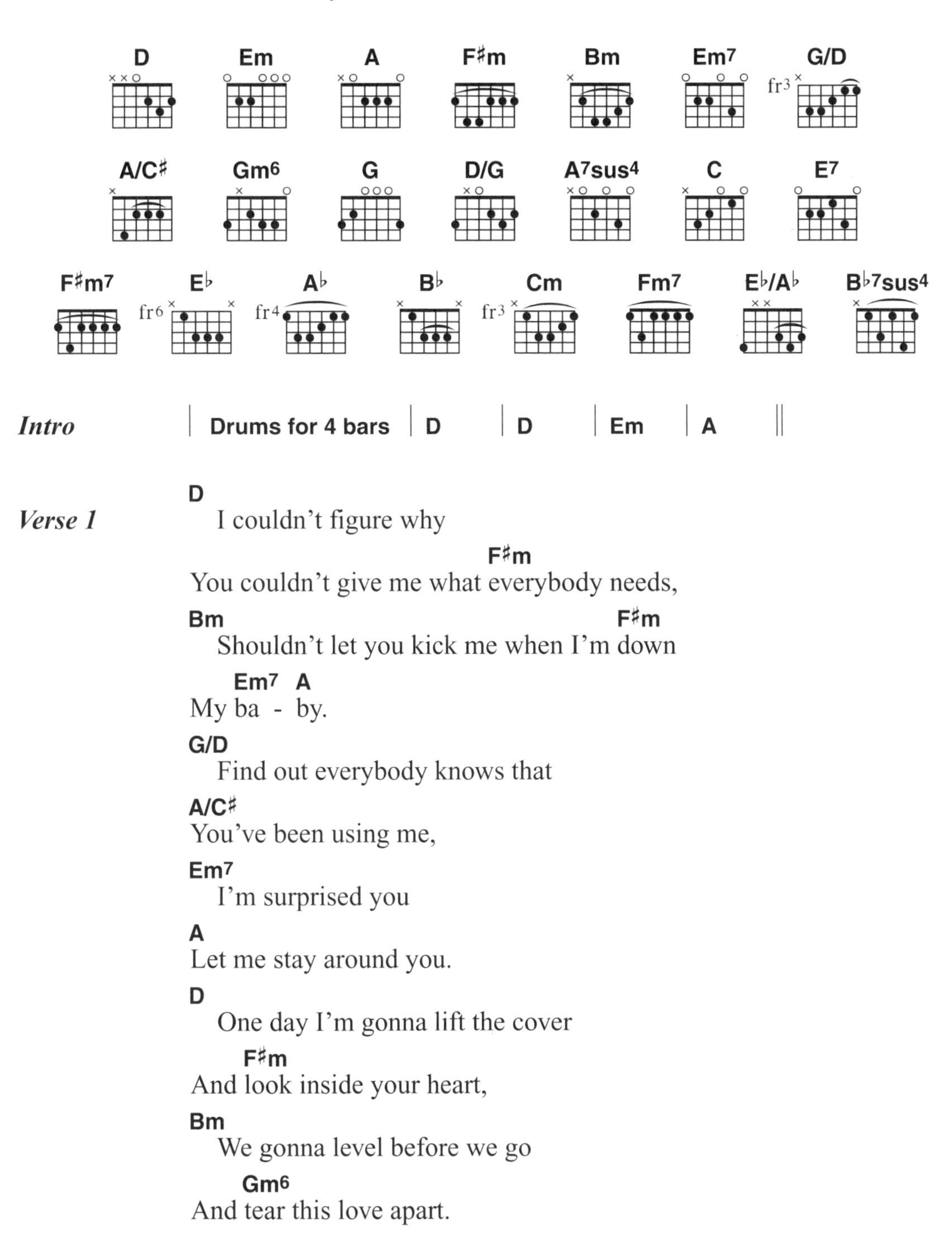

Intro	Drums for 4 bars	D	D	Em	A ‖

Verse 1

D
I couldn't figure why
F♯m
You couldn't give me what everybody needs,
Bm F♯m
Shouldn't let you kick me when I'm down
Em7 A
My ba - by.
G/D
Find out everybody knows that
A/C♯
You've been using me,
Em7
I'm surprised you
A
Let me stay around you.
D
One day I'm gonna lift the cover
F♯m
And look inside your heart,
Bm
We gonna level before we go
Gm6
And tear this love apart.

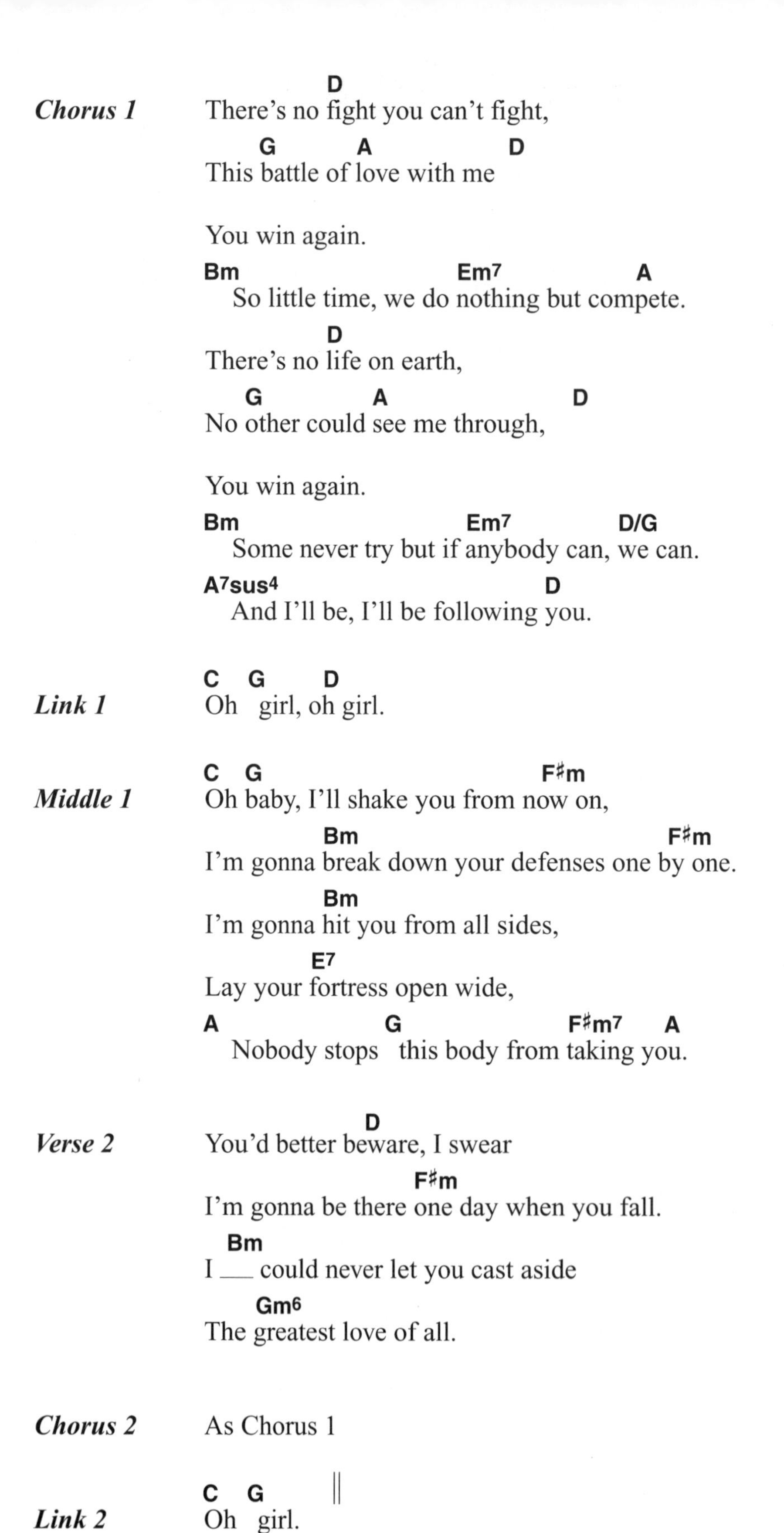

Chorus 1

D
There's no fight you can't fight,
G A D
This battle of love with me

You win again.
Bm Em7 A
So little time, we do nothing but compete.
D
There's no life on earth,
G A D
No other could see me through,

You win again.
Bm Em7 D/G
Some never try but if anybody can, we can.
A7sus4 D
And I'll be, I'll be following you.

Link 1

C G D
Oh girl, oh girl.

Middle 1

C G F♯m
Oh baby, I'll shake you from now on,
Bm F♯m
I'm gonna break down your defenses one by one.
Bm
I'm gonna hit you from all sides,
E7
Lay your fortress open wide,
A G F♯m7 A
Nobody stops this body from taking you.

Verse 2

D
You'd better beware, I swear
F♯m
I'm gonna be there one day when you fall.
Bm
I ___ could never let you cast aside
Gm6
The greatest love of all.

Chorus 2

As Chorus 1

Link 2

C G ‖
Oh girl.

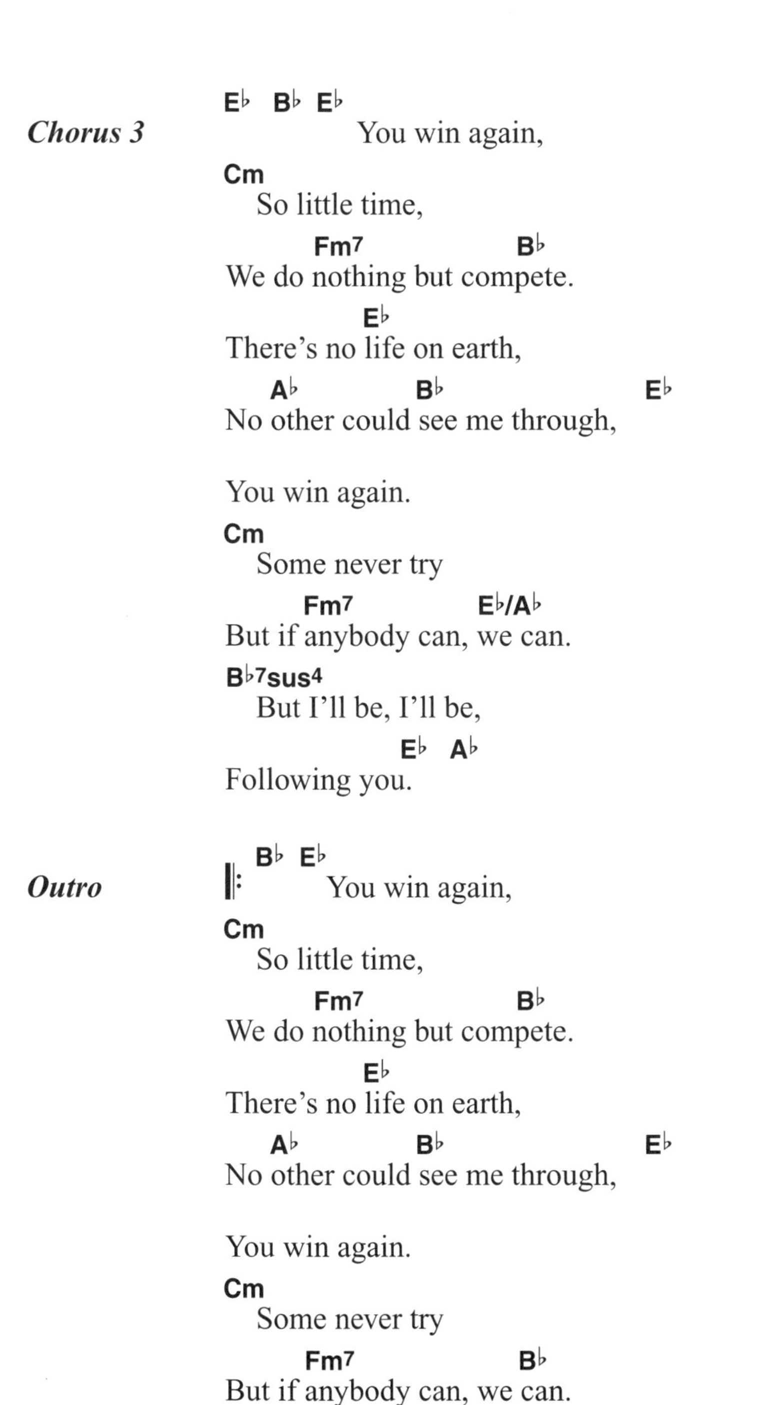

Chorus 3

E♭ B♭ E♭
You win again,
Cm
So little time,
Fm7 B♭
We do nothing but compete.
E♭
There's no life on earth,
A♭ B♭ E♭
No other could see me through,

You win again.
Cm
Some never try
Fm7 E♭/A♭
But if anybody can, we can.
B♭7sus4
But I'll be, I'll be,
E♭ A♭
Following you.

Outro

B♭ E♭
𝄆 You win again,
Cm
So little time,
Fm7 B♭
We do nothing but compete.
E♭
There's no life on earth,
A♭ B♭ E♭
No other could see me through,

You win again.
Cm
Some never try
Fm7 B♭
But if anybody can, we can.
E♭ A♭
There's no fight... 𝄇 *Repeat to fade with vocal ad lib.*

Knowing Me, Knowing You

Words & Music by
Benny Andersson, Björn Ulvaeus & Stig Anderson

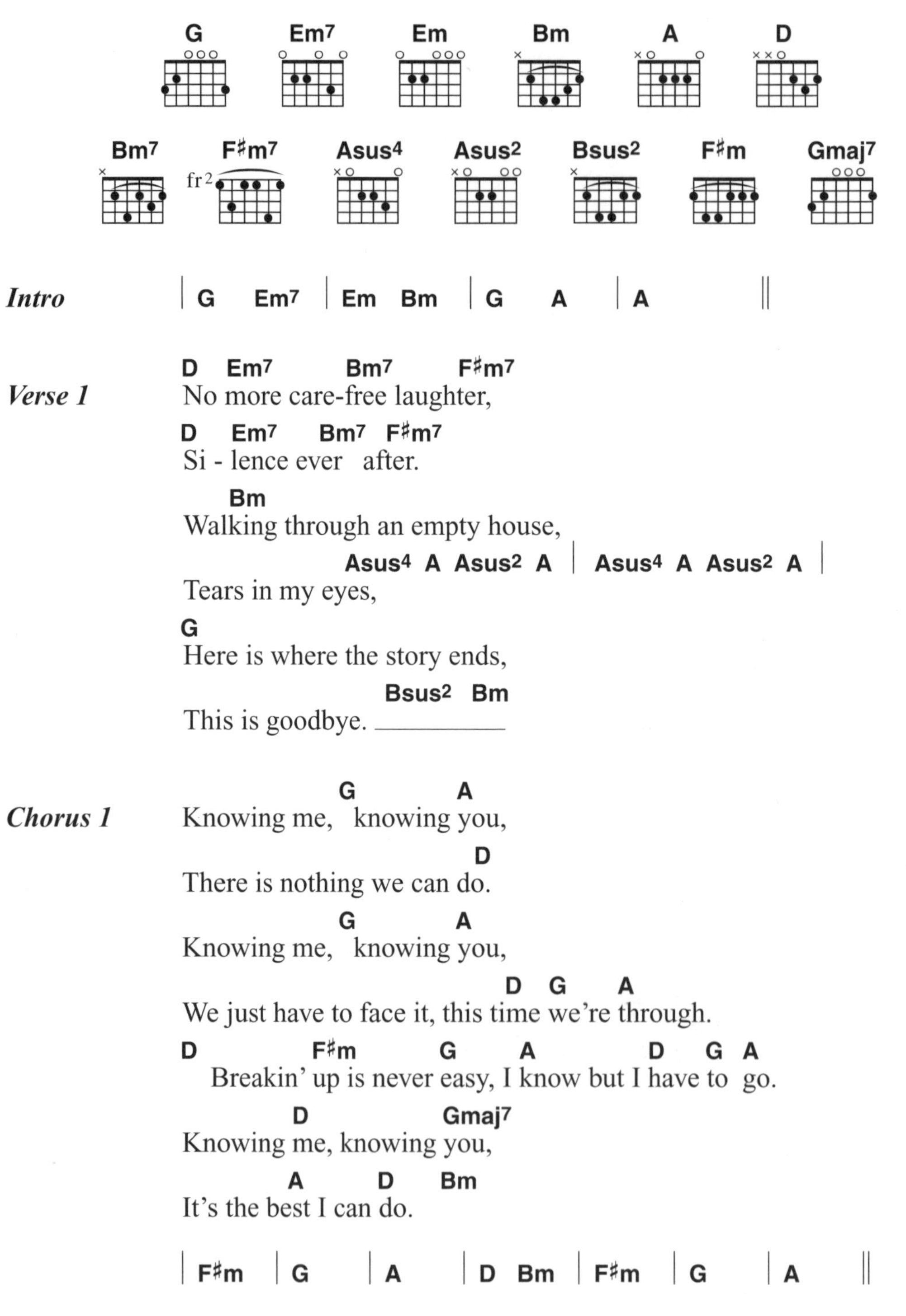

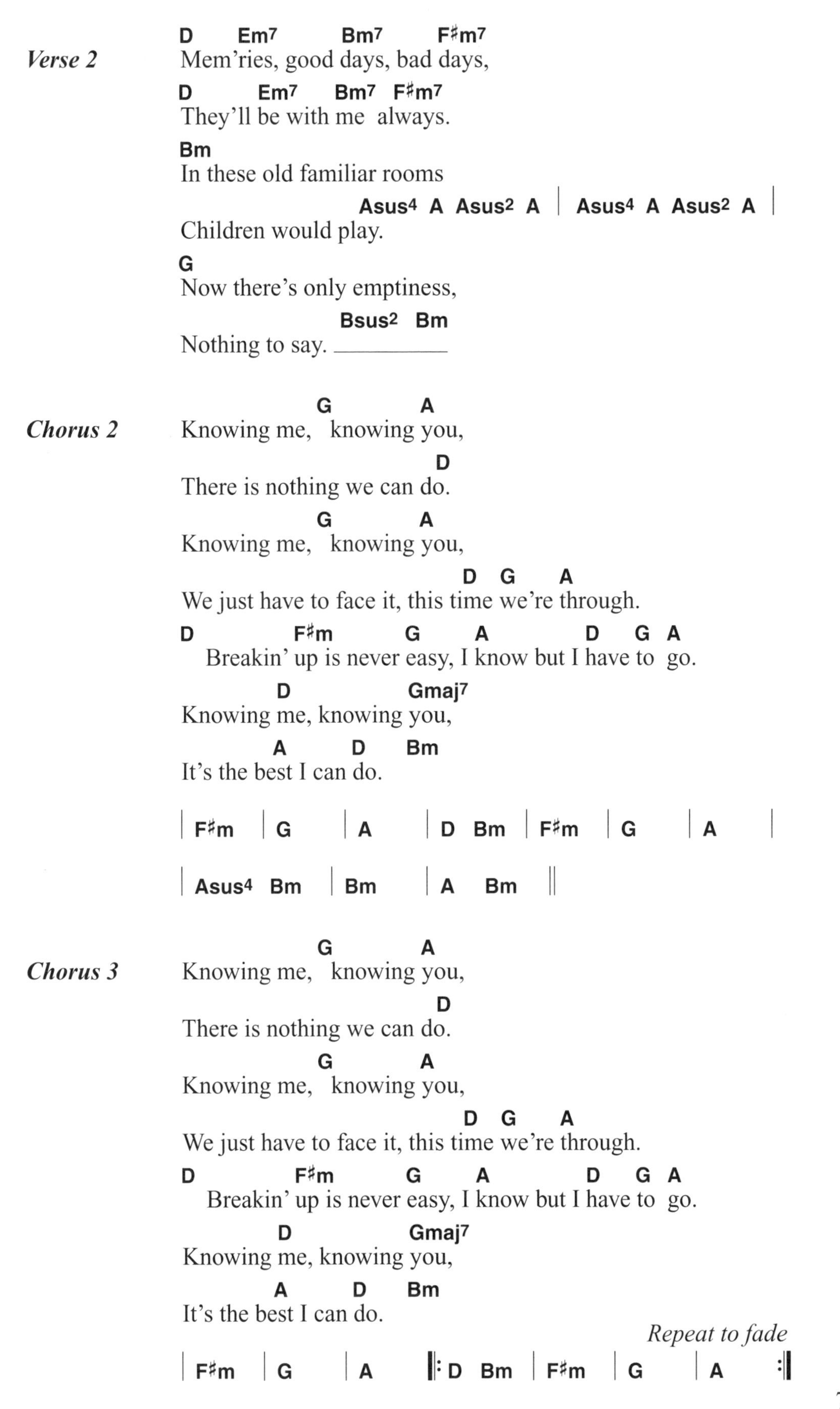
Verse 2
D Em7 Bm7 F#m7
Mem'ries, good days, bad days,
D Em7 Bm7 F#m7
They'll be with me always.
Bm
In these old familiar rooms
Asus4 A Asus2 A | Asus4 A Asus2 A |
Children would play.
G
Now there's only emptiness,
Bsus2 Bm
Nothing to say.
Chorus 2
G A
Knowing me, knowing you,
D
There is nothing we can do.
G A
Knowing me, knowing you,
D G A
We just have to face it, this time we're through.
D F#m G A D G A
Breakin' up is never easy, I know but I have to go.
D Gmaj7
Knowing me, knowing you,
A D Bm
It's the best I can do.
| F#m | G | A | D Bm | F#m | G | A |
| Asus4 Bm | Bm | A Bm ||
Chorus 3
G A
Knowing me, knowing you,
D
There is nothing we can do.
G A
Knowing me, knowing you,
D G A
We just have to face it, this time we're through.
D F#m G A D G A
Breakin' up is never easy, I know but I have to go.
D Gmaj7
Knowing me, knowing you,
A D Bm
It's the best I can do.
Repeat to fade
| F#m | G | A |: D Bm | F#m | G | A :|

Young Guns (Go For It)

Words & Music by
George Michael

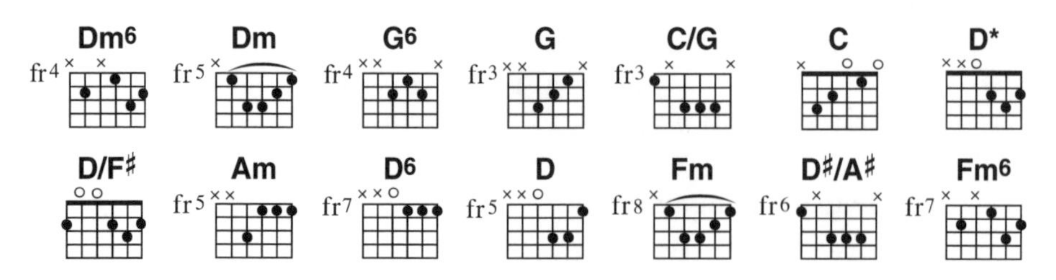

Intro

| Dm6 |

|: Dm G6 | Dm | G6 | G :|

Verse 1

```
N.C.           Dm
Hey suck - er!
                    G6   G
(What the hell's got into you?)
               Dm
Hey suck - er!
                           G6   G
(Now there's nothing you can do.)
          Dm
Well I hadn't seen your face around town awhile

So I greeted you with a knowing smile,
           G6
When I saw that girl upon your arm,
             G
I knew she'd won your heart with a fatal charm.
          Dm
I said, "So boy, let's hit the town!"

I said, "Hey boy, what's with the frown?"
      G6
But in return, all you could say was,
G                          N.C.
"Hi George, meet my fiancée."
```

```
             Dm
Chorus 1     Young Guns,

             Having some fun,
                  C/G
             Cra - zy ladies keep 'em on the run.
             Dm                        C/G
             Wise guys realise there's danger in emotional ties.
             Dm
             See me, single and free,
                C/G
             No fears, no tears, what I want to be.
             Dm
             One, two, take a look at you:
             C/G                     Dm6
             Death by matrimony!


Link 1       ||: Dm  G6 | Dm    | G6    | G     :||


                       Dm
Verse 2      Hey suck - er!
                                      G6    G
             (What the hell's got into you?)
                       Dm
             Hey suck - er!
                                            G6    G
             (Now there's nothing you can do.)
               Dm
             A married man? You're out of your head,

             Sleepless nights on an H.P. bed.
               G6
             A daddy by the time you're twenty-one,
                     G6
             If you're happy with a nappy then you're in for fun.
                       Dm
             But you're here,

             And you're there,

             Well, there's guys like you just everywhere.
             G6
             Looking back on the good old days?
                  G
             Well, this young gun says, "Caution pays!"
```

Chorus 2

Dm
Young Guns,

Having some fun,

C/G
Cra - zy ladies keep 'em on the run.

Dm C/G
Wise guys realise there's danger in emotional ties.

Dm
See me, single and free,

C/G
No fears, no tears, what I want to be.

Dm
One, two, take a look at you:

C/G Dm6
Death by matrimony!

Bridge

C
I remember when we such fun and everything was fine,

D* D/F♯
I remember when we use to have a good time,

Partners in crime.

C
Tell me that's all in the past and I will gladly walk away,

D*
Tell me that you're happy now,

D/F♯
Turning my back,

C
Nothing to say!

Verse 3

Am
"Hey, tell this jerk to take a hike,

There's somethin' 'bout that boy I don't like."

D6
"Well, sugar he don't mean the things he said,"

D
"Just get him outta my way, 'cos I'm seeing red.

Am
We got plans to make, we got things to buy,

cont. And you're wasting time on some creepy guy."

```
     D6
"Hey shut up chick, that's a friend of mine,
    D
Just watch your mouth babe, you're out of line."
```

Break

```
N.C.
Ooooooh!
   Fm
||: Get back!

Hands off!

Go for it!
D♯/B♭
Get back!

Hands off! :|| (Play 4 times)
```

Chorus 3

```
Fm
Young Guns,

Having some fun,
         D♯/A♯
Cra - zy ladies keep 'em on the run.
Fm                             D♯/A♯
Wise guys realise there's danger in emotional ties.
Fm
See me, single and free,
     D♯/A♯
No fears, no tears, what I want to be.
Fm
One, two, take a look at you:
D♯/A♯                     Fm6
Death by matrimony!
```

Back For Good

Words & Music by
Gary Barlow

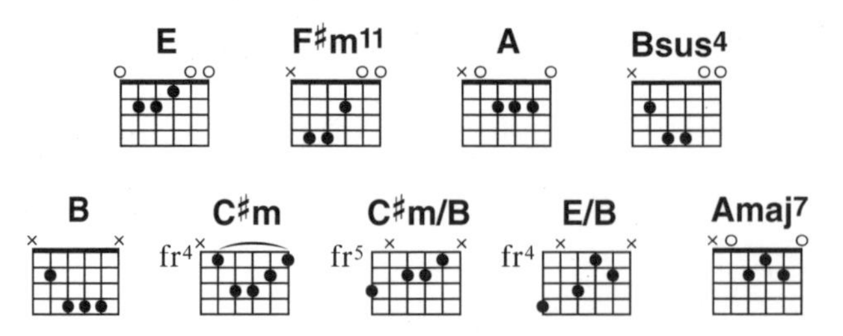

Capo first fret

Intro |: E | F♯m11 | A | Bsus4 B :| B | B ||

Verse 1

E F♯m11 A B E
I guess now it's time for me to give up,
F♯m11 A B
I feel it's time.
E F♯m11
Got a picture of you beside me,
A B E F♯m11 A Bsus4
Got your lipstick mark still on your coffee cup, oh, yeah.
B E F♯m11
Got a fist of pure emotion,
A B
Got a head of shattered dreams,
C♯m C♯m/B E/B A Bsus4 B
Gotta leave it, gotta leave it all behind now.

Chorus 1

E F♯m11 A
Whatever I said, whatever I did I didn't mean it,
B E F♯m11 A Bsus4 B
I just want you back for good.
E F♯m11 A
Whenever I'm wrong just tell me the song and I'll sing it,
B E F♯m11
You'll be right and understood.
A Bsus4 B
I want you back for good.

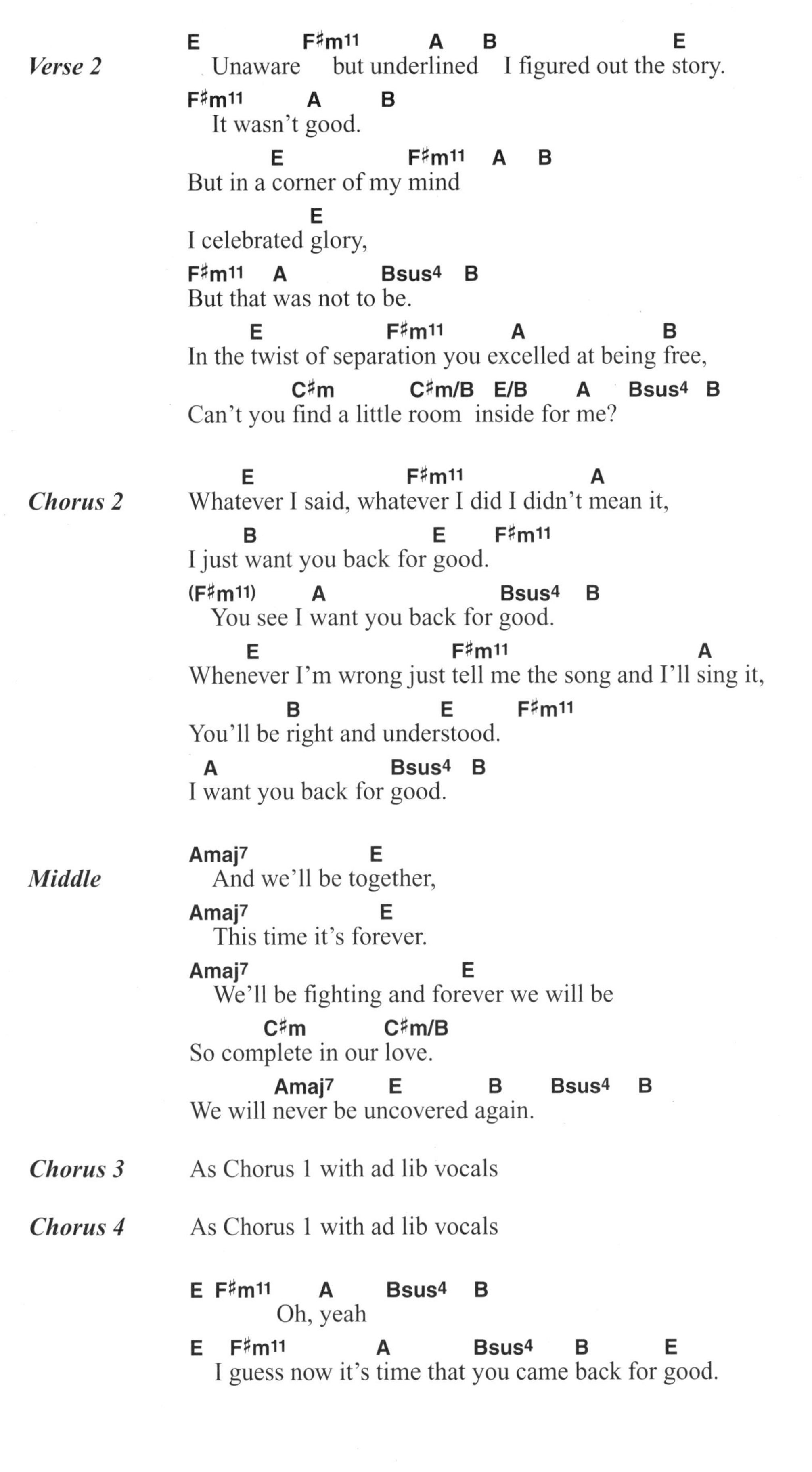
Verse 2
E F♯m11 A B E
Unaware but underlined I figured out the story.
F♯m11 A B
It wasn't good.
E F♯m11 A B
But in a corner of my mind
E
I celebrated glory,
F♯m11 A Bsus4 B
But that was not to be.
E F♯m11 A B
In the twist of separation you excelled at being free,
C♯m C♯m/B E/B A Bsus4 B
Can't you find a little room inside for me?
Chorus 2
E F♯m11 A
Whatever I said, whatever I did I didn't mean it,
B E F♯m11
I just want you back for good.
(F♯m11) A Bsus4 B
You see I want you back for good.
E F♯m11 A
Whenever I'm wrong just tell me the song and I'll sing it,
B E F♯m11
You'll be right and understood.
A Bsus4 B
I want you back for good.
Middle
Amaj7 E
And we'll be together,
Amaj7 E
This time it's forever.
Amaj7 E
We'll be fighting and forever we will be
C♯m C♯m/B
So complete in our love.
Amaj7 E B Bsus4 B
We will never be uncovered again.
Chorus 3
As Chorus 1 with ad lib vocals
Chorus 4
As Chorus 1 with ad lib vocals
E F♯m11 A Bsus4 B
Oh, yeah
E F♯m11 A Bsus4 B E
I guess now it's time that you came back for good.

Flying Without Wings

Words & Music by
Steve Mac & Wayne Hector

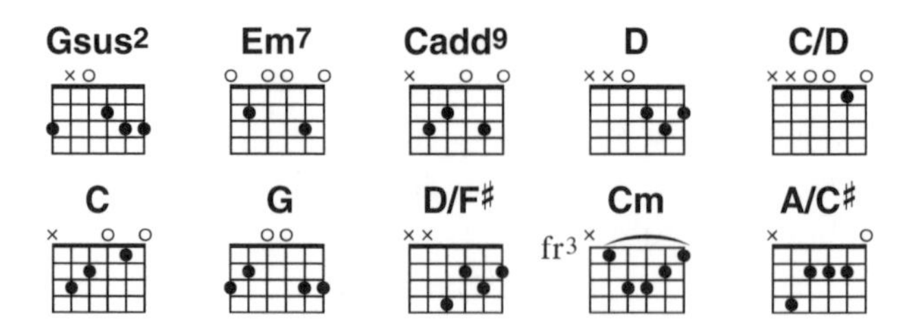

Capo 1st Fret

Verse 1

```
N.C.                            Gsus2
Everybody's looking for that something,
                              Em7
One thing that makes it all complete,
                              Cadd9
You find it in the strangest places,
                              D
Places you never knew it could be.

                              Gsus2
Some find it in the face of their children,
                              Em7
Some find it in their lover's eyes.
                              Cadd9
Who can deny the joy it brings,
                                    D
When you've found that special thing,
                         G
You're flying without wings.
```

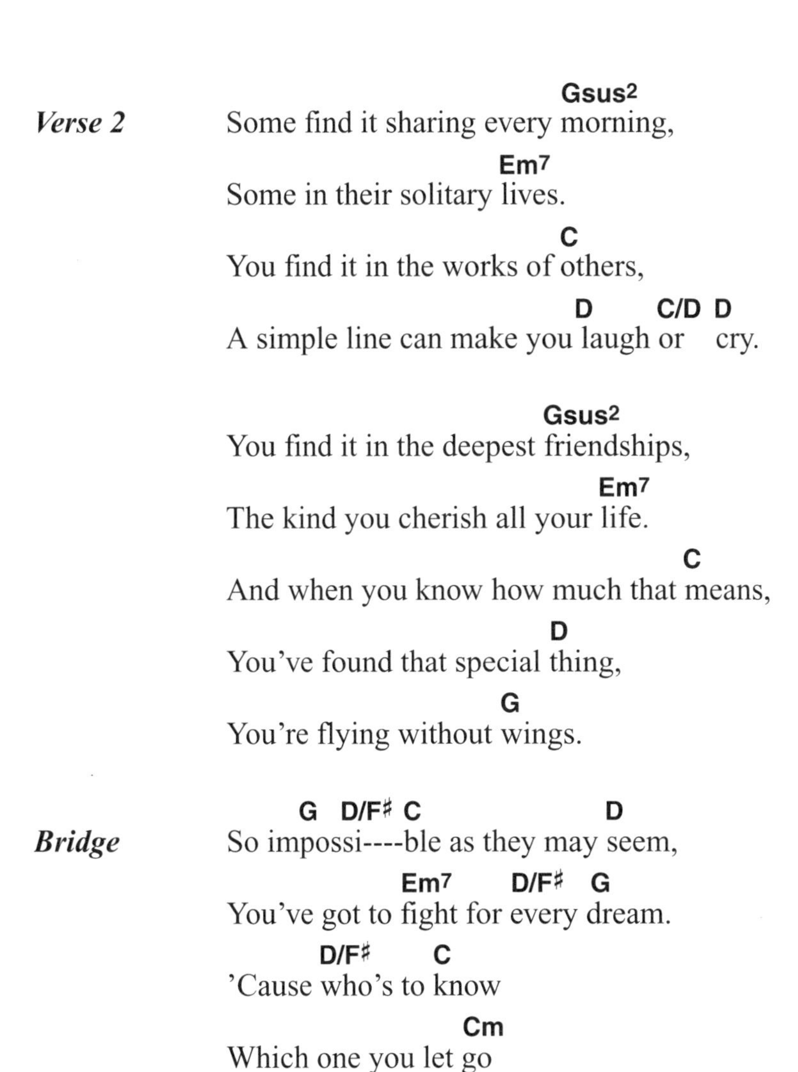

Verse 2

Gsus2
Some find it sharing every morning,
Em7
Some in their solitary lives.
C
You find it in the works of others,
D C/D D
A simple line can make you laugh or cry.

Gsus2
You find it in the deepest friendships,
Em7
The kind you cherish all your life.
C
And when you know how much that means,
D
You've found that special thing,
G
You're flying without wings.

Bridge

G D/F♯ C D
So impossi----ble as they may seem,
Em7 D/F♯ G
You've got to fight for every dream.
D/F♯ C
'Cause who's to know
Cm
Which one you let go
C/D D
Would have made you complete.

Verse 3

C/D D Gsus2
Well for me it's waking up beside you,

D/F♯ Em7
To watch the sun rise on your face.

C
To know that I can say I love you,

D
At any given time or place.

Gsus2
It's little things that only I know,

D/F♯ Em7
Those are the things that make you mine.

C
And it's like flying without wings,

D
'Cause you're my special thing,

Gsus2
I'm flying without wings.

Outro

D/F♯ C
And you're the place my life begins,

D
And you'll be where it ends,

C
I'm flying without wings,

A/C♯ C/D
And that's the joy you bring,

G
I'm flying without wings.

Stars

Words & Music by
Mick Hucknall

Gsus2 G B7sus4 B7 Bm7 Am7

Intro ‖: Gsus2 G | Gsus2 G | B7sus4 | B7 :‖

Verse 1

G Bm7
Anyone who ever held you
Am7 B7sus4 B7
Would tell you the way I'm feeling,
G Bm7
Anyone who ever wanted you
Am7 B7sus4 B7
Would try to tell you what I feel in - side.
G Bm7
The only thing I ever wanted
Am7 B7sus4 B7
Was the feeling that you ain't faking,
G Bm7
The only one you ever thought about,
Am7 B7sus4 B7
Wait a minute, can't you see that

Chorus 1

G Bm7 Am7
I______ wanna fall from the stars
B7sus4 B7
Straight into your arms.
G Bm7 Am7
I,______ I feel you,
B7sus4 B7
I hope you compre - hend.

Link | Gsus2 G | Gsus2 G | B7sus4 B7 ||

Verse 2

G Bm7
For the man who tried to hurt you,
Am7 B7sus4 B7
He's explaining the way I'm feeling.
G Bm7
For all the jealousy I caused you
Am7 B7sus4 B7
States the reason why I'm trying to hide.
G Bm7
As for all the things you taught me,
Am7 B7sus4 B7
It sends my future into clearer di - mensions.
G Bm7
You'll never know how much you hurt me,
Am7 B7sus4 B7
Stay a minute, can't you see that

Chorus 2

G Bm7 Am7
I—— wanna fall from the stars
B7sus4 B7
Straight into your arms.
G Bm7 Am7
I,—— I feel you,
B7sus4 B7
I hope you compre - hend.

Instrumental

Gsus2 G	Gsus2 G	B7sus4	B7
Gsus2 G	Gsus2 G	B7sus4	B7
Gsus2 G	Gsus2 G	B7sus4	B7	

Verse 3

G Bm7
Too many hearts are broken,

Am7 B7sus4 B7
A lover's promise never came with a maybe.

G Bm7
So many words are left un - spoken,

Am7 B7sus4 B7
The silent voices are driving me crazy.

G Bm7
After all the pain you caused me,

Am7 B7sus4 B7
Making up could never be your in - tention.

G Bm7
You'll never know how much you hurt me,

Am7 B7sus4 B7
Stay, can't you see that

Chorus 3

G Bm7 Am7
I______ wanna fall from the stars

B7sus4 B7
Straight into your arms.

G Bm7 Am7
I,______ I feel you,

B7sus4 B7
I hope you compre - hend.

G Bm7 Am7
That I______ wanna fall from the stars

B7sus4 B7
Straight into your arms.

G Bm7 Am7
I,______ I feel you,

B7sus4
I hope you comprehend.

Son Of A Preacher Man

Words & Music by
John Hurley & Ronnie Wilkins

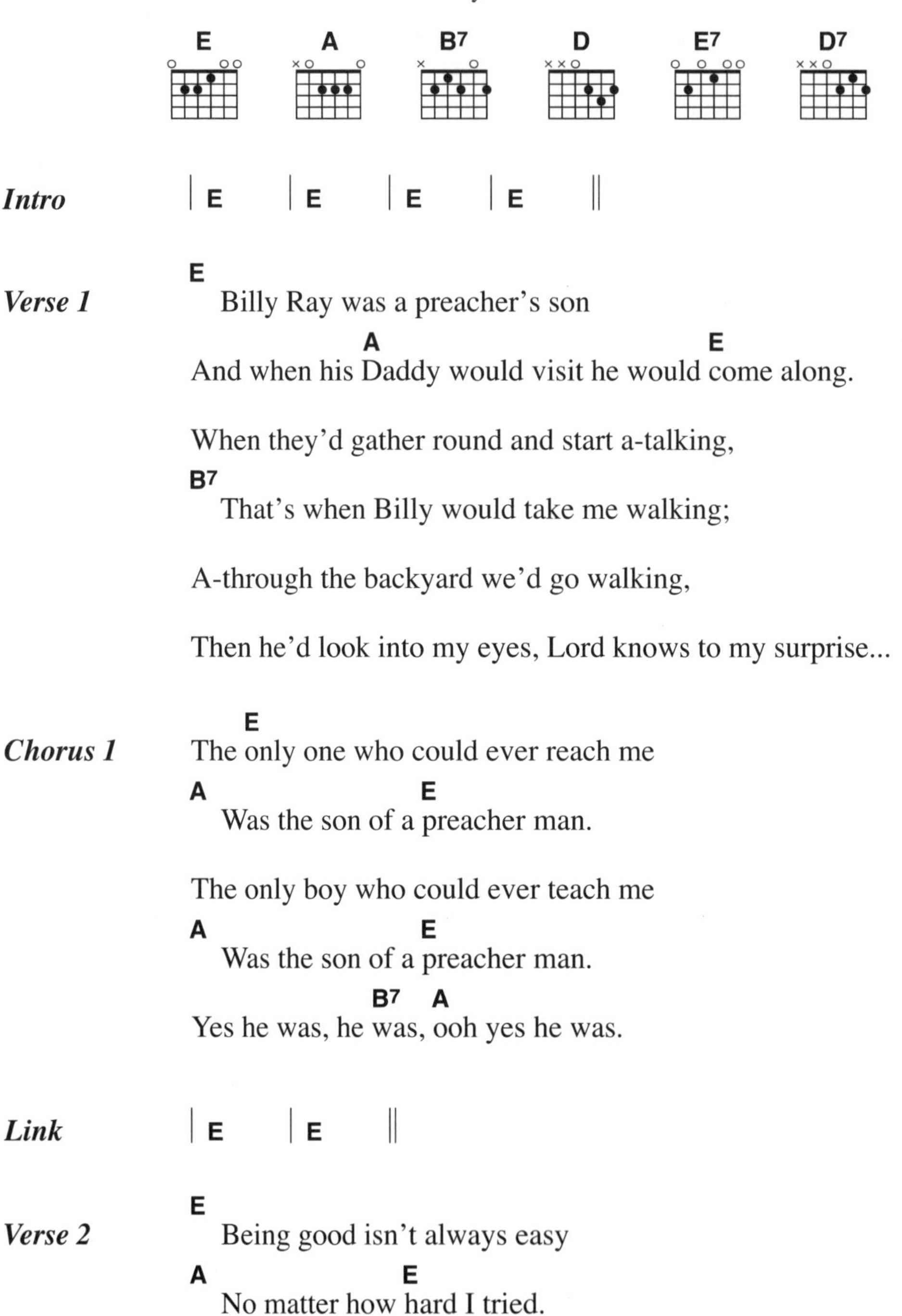

Intro | E | E | E | E ||

Verse 1

E
Billy Ray was a preacher's son
A E
And when his Daddy would visit he would come along.
When they'd gather round and start a-talking,
B7
That's when Billy would take me walking;
A-through the backyard we'd go walking,
Then he'd look into my eyes, Lord knows to my surprise...

Chorus 1

E
The only one who could ever reach me
A E
Was the son of a preacher man.
The only boy who could ever teach me
A E
Was the son of a preacher man.
B7 A
Yes he was, he was, ooh yes he was.

Link | E | E ||

Verse 2

E
Being good isn't always easy
A E
No matter how hard I tried.

cont.

When he started sweet-talking to me,

B7
He'd come and tell me everything is alright,

He keeps on telling me everything is alright,

Can I get away again tonight?

Chorus 2

E
The only one who could ever reach me

A E
Was the son of a preacher man.

The only boy who could ever teach me

A E
Was the son of a preacher man.

B7 A D
Yes he was, he was, ooh, Lord knows he was (yes he was.)

Bridge

D A
How well I remember the look was in his eyes,

Stealing kisses from me on the sly.

B7
Taking time to make time,

Telling me that he's all mine;

E7
Learning from each other's knowing,

Looking to see how much we're growing.

Chorus 3

A
The only one who could ever reach me

D A
Was the son of a preacher man.

The only boy who could ever teach me

D A
Was the son of a preacher man.

E7 D7
Yes he was, he was, ooh yes he was.

Chorus 4

As Chorus 3
With vocal ad lib.

Thank You

Words & Music by
Dido Armstrong & Paul Herman

Em C D G G/F♯ G/B C/D Am

Capo fourth fret

Intro ‖: Em | C | Em | C :‖ *Play 4 times*

Verse 1

```
Em                C
   My tea's gone cold
                D          G       G/F♯  Em
I'm wondering why I got out of bed at all,
               C                  D
The morning rain clouds up my window,
      G       G/F♯  Em
And I can't see at all.
          C            D
And even if I could it'd all be grey
            G        G/F♯   Em
But your picture on my wall
      C                Em
It re - minds me that it's not so bad,
    C          | Em     | C      | Em     | C      |
It's not so bad.
```

Verse 2

```
Em          C
   I drank too much last night,
    D               G          G/F♯   Em
Got bills to pay, my head just feels in pain.
              C                    D
I missed the bus and they'll be hell today,
    G      G/F♯       Em
I'm late for work a - gain.
          C                  D
And even if I'm there, they'll all imply
```

cont.

```
      G           G/F♯    Em
That I might not last the day,
                     C
And then you'll call me
          Em
And it's not so bad,
     C
It's not so bad.
```

Chorus 1

```
    G G/B     C
And I  want to thank you
    C/D             G         G/B   C    C/D
For giving me the best day of my life,
    G  G/B    C
And oh, just to be with you
  C/D         G/B               Am
Is having the best day of my life.
```

Interlude

| G G/B | C C/D | G G/B | C C/D |

| G G/B | C | G/B | Am ||

Verse 3

```
G                         G/B      C
   Push the door, I'm home at last
                     C/D          G
And I'm soaking through and through.
                     G/B  C
Then you handed me a towel,
          C/D  G
And all I see is you.
                   G/B          C
And even if my house falls down now
           C/D    G/B
I wouldn't have a clue
                   Am
Because you're near me.
```

Chorus 2 As Chorus 1

Chorus 3 As Chorus 1

Beautiful

Words & Music by
Linda Perry

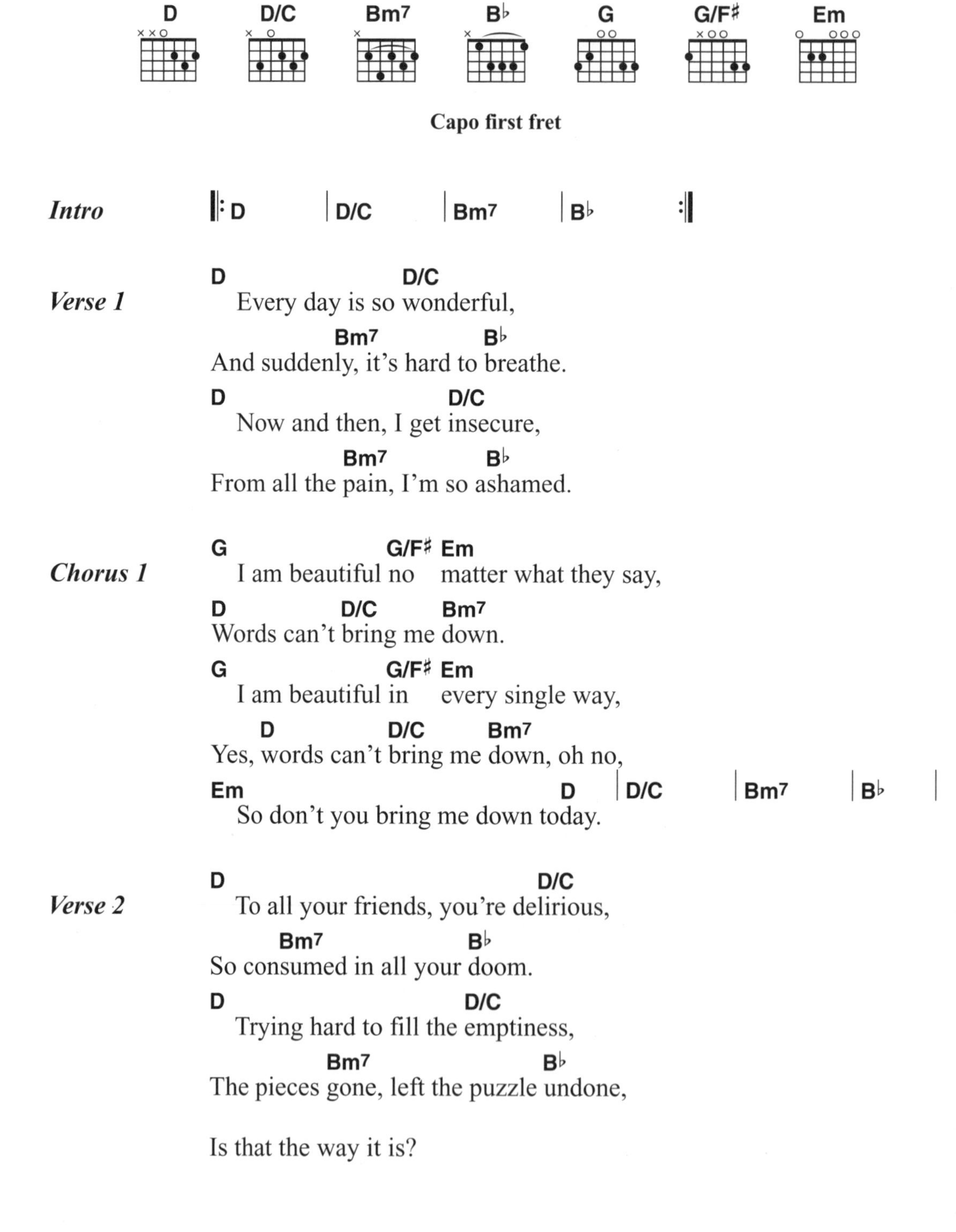

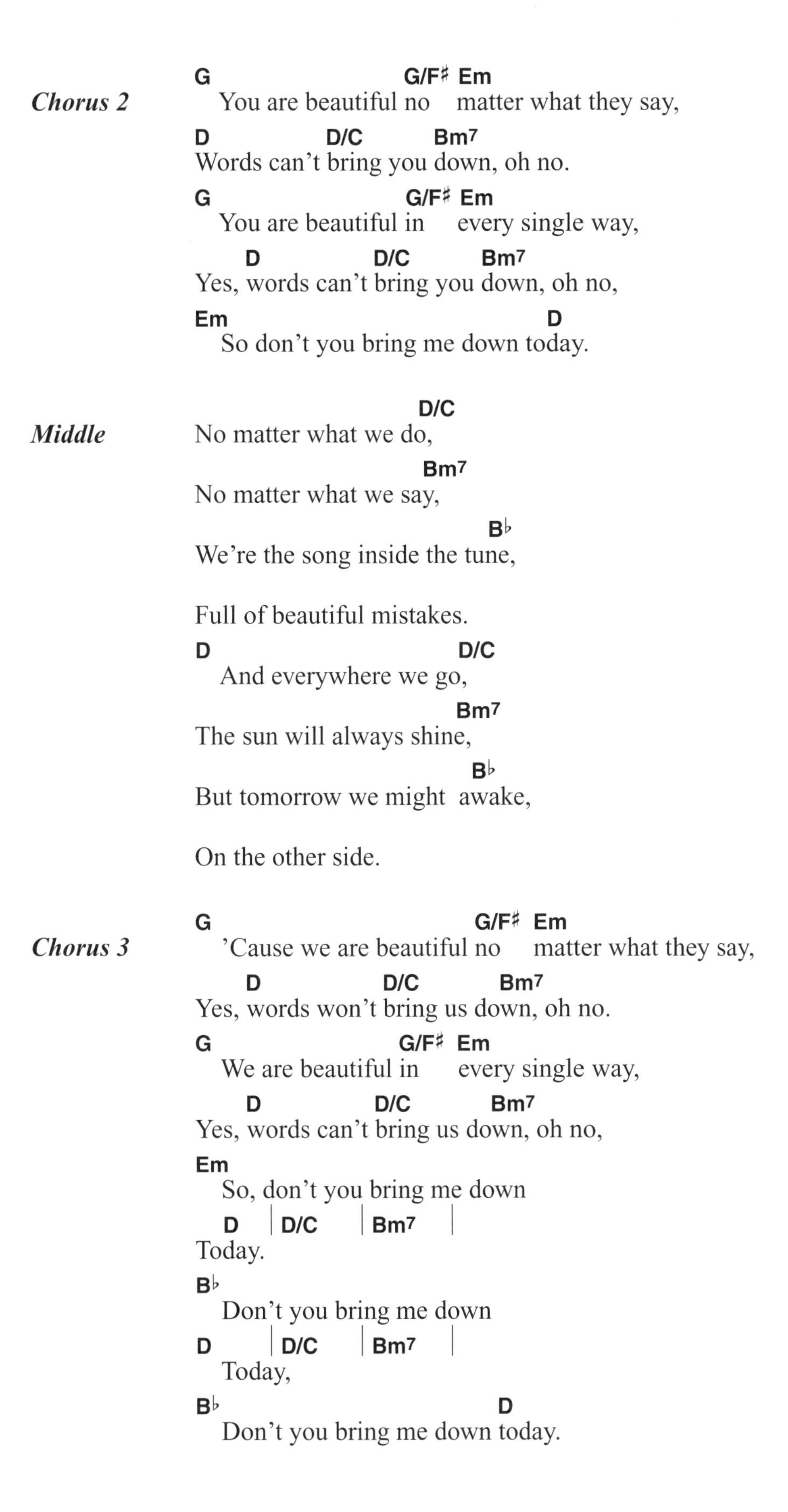

Chorus 2

G G/F♯ Em
You are beautiful no matter what they say,
D D/C Bm7
Words can't bring you down, oh no.
G G/F♯ Em
You are beautiful in every single way,
D D/C Bm7
Yes, words can't bring you down, oh no,
Em D
So don't you bring me down today.

Middle

D/C
No matter what we do,
Bm7
No matter what we say,
B♭
We're the song inside the tune,

Full of beautiful mistakes.
D D/C
And everywhere we go,
Bm7
The sun will always shine,
B♭
But tomorrow we might awake,

On the other side.

Chorus 3

G G/F♯ Em
'Cause we are beautiful no matter what they say,
D D/C Bm7
Yes, words won't bring us down, oh no.
G G/F♯ Em
We are beautiful in every single way,
D D/C Bm7
Yes, words can't bring us down, oh no,
Em
So, don't you bring me down
D | D/C | Bm7 |
Today.
B♭
Don't you bring me down
D | D/C | Bm7 |
Today,
B♭ D
Don't you bring me down today.

I'm Outta Love

Words & Music by
Anastacia, Sam Watters & Louis Biancaniello

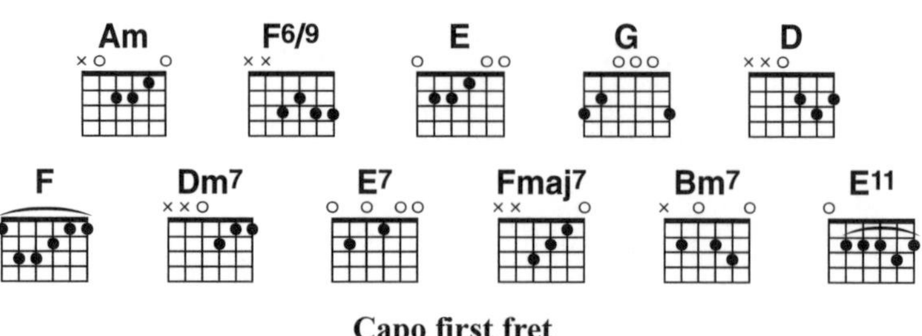

Capo first fret

Intro ||: Am | Am | F6/9 | F6/9 :||

```
           Am    E
Oooaaah,
G            D
Whoh,        yeah, yeah, yeah, yeah,
Am         E
      Oh yeah,
G            D
      Uh-huh.
```

Verse 1

```
Am                    E
   Now baby, come on,
        G                        D            Am
Don't claim that love you never let me feel.
            E
I shoulda known
       G                         D
'Cos you've brought nothing real,
                 Am
Come on be a man about it,
E
You won't die,
F                      Dm7      E7
I ain't got no more tears to cry.
       Am              E
And I can't take this no more,
                F         E
You know, I gotta let it go.

And you know,
```

```
             N.C.      Am
Chorus 1     I'm outta love,

                       E
             Set me free

                            G              D
             And let me out this mis - ery.

                                     Am              E
             Just show me the way to get my life again

             N.C. G                    D
             'Cos you can't handle me.

                                 Am
             Said, I'm outta love,

                          E
             Can't you see

                          F                 E
             Baby, that you gotta set me free?

                                Am
             I'm outta love,          yeah.


             Am                     E
Verse 2         Said, how many times

             G               D                Am
             Have I tried to turn this love a - round?

                          E
             But every time

             G                D
             You just let me down.

                                Am
             Come on, be a man about it,

             E
             You'll survive,

             F                               Dm7    E7
             True that you can work it out all right.

                        Am
             Tell me, yesterday,

                         E
             Did you know

                         F           E
             I'd be the one to let you go?

             And you know,
```

```
            N.C.        Am
Chorus 2    I'm outta love

                      E
            Set me free

                         G                   D
            And let me out this mis - ery

                                    Am                   E
            Just show me the way to get my life again

            G                   D
            You can't handle me

                               Am
            Said, I'm outta love

                         E
            Can't you see

                         F                         E
            Baby that you gotta set me free?

            I'm outta...


            Fmaj7
Bridge        Let me get over you

            E7
              The way you've gotten over me too, yeah.

            Fmaj7
              Seems like my time has come

                Bm7                   E11
            And now I'm moving on,

            I'll be stronger.
```

Chorus 3

(Am)
I'm outta love,

(E)
Set me free

(G) (D)
And let me out this mis - ery.

(Am) (E)
Show me the way to get my life again

(G) (D)
You can't handle me.

Am E
Said, I'm outta love , set me free

G D
And let me out this mis - ery.

Am E
Show me the way to get my life again,

G D
You can't handle me.

Am E
Said I'm outta love, can't you see

G D
Baby that you gotta set me free?

Am
I'm outta love,

N.C.
Yeah, yeah, yeah, yeah.

Am E
I'm outta love, set me free

G D
And let me out this mis - ery

Am E
Just show me the way to get my life again

G D
You can't handle me

Am
(I said) I'm outta love

E
Set me free

G D
And let me out this mis - ery

Fade

No Ordinary Love

Words & Music by
Adu & Matthewman

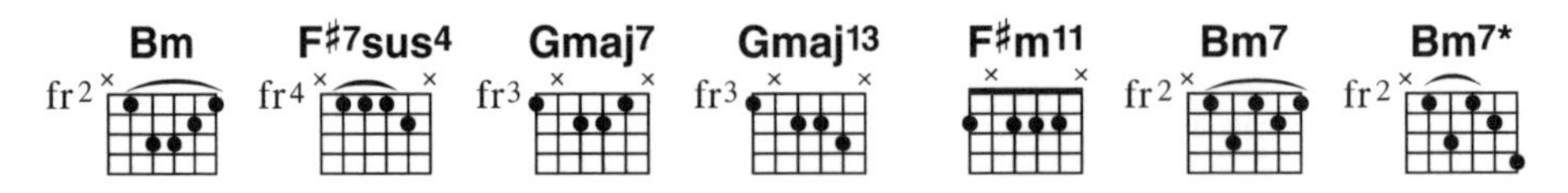

Intro | Bm | F♯7sus4 | Gmaj7 | Gmaj13 |
| Gmaj7 | F♯m11 | Bm7 | Bm7* ||

Verse 1

                  Bm
I gave you all the love I got,
                  F♯7sus4
I gave you more than I could give,
Gmaj7   Gmaj13
   I gave you love.
                  Gmaj7
I gave you all that I have inside,
              F♯m11
And you took my love,
              Bm7   Bm7*
You took   my love.
             Bm
Didn't I tell you
                   F♯7sus4
What I be - lieve?
                        Gmaj7
Did somebody say that
   Gmaj13
A love like that won't last?
             Gmaj7
Didn't I give you
                    F♯m11   Bm7   Bm7*
All that I've got to give, ba - by?

Verse 2

Bm
I gave you all the love I got,
F♯7sus4
I gave you more than I could give,
Gmaj7 Gmaj13
I gave you love.
Gmaj7
I gave you all that I have inside,
F♯m11
And you took my love,
Bm7
You took my love.

Pre-chorus 1

Bm F♯7sus4
I keep crying,
Gmaj7 Gmaj13
I keep trying for you,
Gmaj7 F♯m11 Bm7 Bm7*
There's nothing like you and I ba - by.

Chorus 1

Bm
This is no ordinary love,
F♯7sus4 Gmaj7 Gmaj13
No ordinary love.
Gmaj7
This is no ordinary love,
F♯m11 Bm7 Bm7*
No ordinary love.

Verse 3

Gmaj7 F♯m11
When you came my way
Bm7
You brightened every day
Gmaj7 F♯m11 Bm7
With your sweet smile.
Bm
Didn't I tell you
F♯7sus4
What I be - lieve?
Gmaj7
Did somebody say that
Gmaj13
A love like that won't last?
Gmaj7
Didn't I give you
F♯m11 Bm7 Bm7*
All that I've got to give, ba - by?

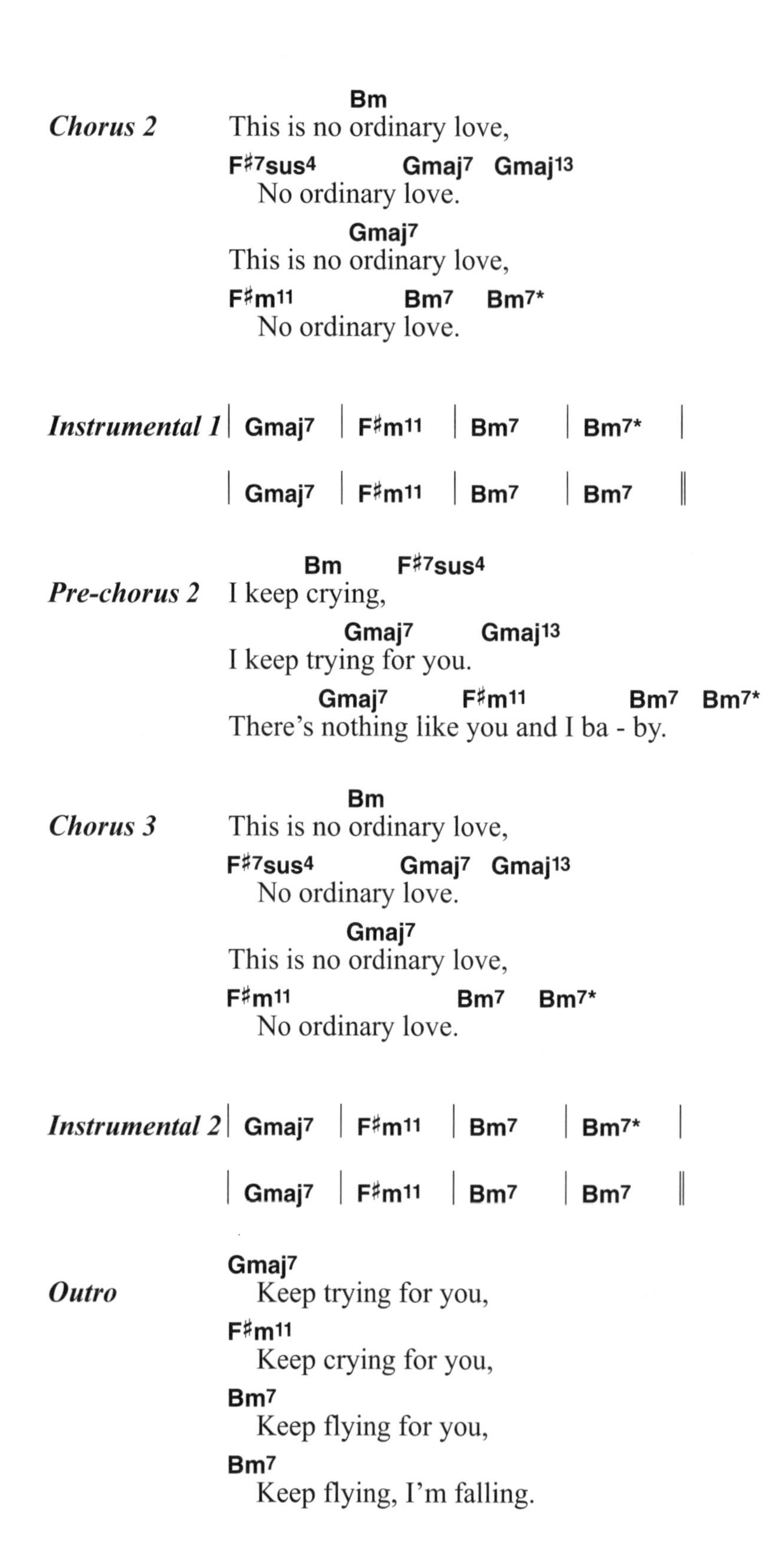

Chorus 2

Bm
This is no ordinary love,
F♯7sus4 Gmaj7 Gmaj13
No ordinary love.
Gmaj7
This is no ordinary love,
F♯m11 Bm7 Bm7*
No ordinary love.

Instrumental 1 | Gmaj7 | F♯m11 | Bm7 | Bm7* |
| Gmaj7 | F♯m11 | Bm7 | Bm7 ||

Pre-chorus 2

Bm F♯7sus4
I keep crying,
Gmaj7 Gmaj13
I keep trying for you.
Gmaj7 F♯m11 Bm7 Bm7*
There's nothing like you and I ba - by.

Chorus 3

Bm
This is no ordinary love,
F♯7sus4 Gmaj7 Gmaj13
No ordinary love.
Gmaj7
This is no ordinary love,
F♯m11 Bm7 Bm7*
No ordinary love.

Instrumental 2 | Gmaj7 | F♯m11 | Bm7 | Bm7* |
| Gmaj7 | F♯m11 | Bm7 | Bm7 ||

Outro

Gmaj7
Keep trying for you,
F♯m11
Keep crying for you,
Bm7
Keep flying for you,
Bm7
Keep flying, I'm falling.

cont. | Gmaj7 | F♯m11 | Bm7 | Bm7 |

| Gmaj7 | F♯m11 | Bm7 | Bm7 ||

Gmaj7 F♯m11 Bm7
And I'm falling—

Gmaj7
Keep trying for you,

F♯m11
Keep crying for you,

Bm7
Keep flying for you,

Bm7
Keep flying, I'm falling...

| Gmaj7 | F♯m11 | Bm7 | Bm7 |

Gmaj7 | F♯m11 | Bm7* | Bm7* |
And I'm falling.—

Outro ||: Gmaj7 | F♯m11 | Bm7 | Bm7 :|| *To fade*

Independent Women Part I

Words & Music by
Beyonce Knowles, Samuel Barnes, Corey Rooney & Jean Claude Olivier

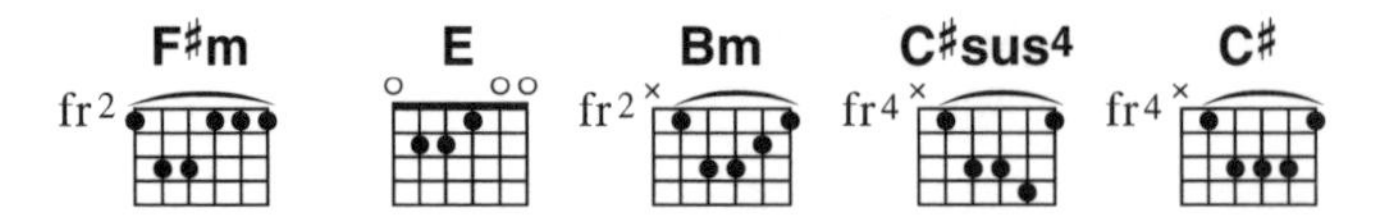

Intro

F♯m E F♯m

F♯m E F♯m
Lucy Liu
F♯m E F♯m
With my girl, Drew
F♯m E F♯m
Cameron D and Destiny
F♯m E F♯m
Charlie's Angels, come on,
F♯m E F♯ N.C.
Uh, uh, uh.

F♯m E F♯m

Verse 1

N.C. F♯m E F♯m
Question: Tell me what you think a - bout me?
F♯m E F♯m
I buy my own diamonds and I buy my own rings,
F♯m E F♯m
Only ring your cell-y when I'm feel - in' lonely,
F♯m E F♯m
When it's all over please get up and leave.
N.C. F♯m E F♯m
Question: Tell me how you feel a - bout this?
F♯m E F♯m
Try to con - trol me boy you get dis - missed,
F♯m E F♯m
Pay my own car note and I pay my own bills,
F♯m E F♯m
Always fifty-fifty in rela - tion - ships.

```
            Bm          F♯m  Bm
cont.       The shoes on my    feet

            (I've bought it)
                 F♯m           E        F♯m
            The clothes I'm wear - ing

            (I've bought it)
                 Bm          F♯m   Bm
            The rock I'm rock - in'

            (I've bought it)
                  F♯m        E   F♯m
            'Cos I depend on me
                              Bm               F♯m    Bm
            If I wanted the watch you're wear - in'

            (I'll buy it)
                 F♯m      E    F♯m
            The house I live in

            (I've bought it)
                 Bm       F♯m   Bm
            The car I'm driv - ing

            (I've bought it)
            C♯sus4      C♯
            I depend on me

            (I depend on me).

            F♯m              E      F♯m
Chorus 1    All the wo - men        who independent
            F♯m                      E  F♯m
            (Throw your hands up at me)
            F♯m              E    F♯m
            All the hon - eys         who makin' money
            F♯m                      E      F♯m
            (Throw your hands up at me)
            Bm                 F♯m  Bm
            All the mom - mas       who profit dollas
            F♯m                      E  F♯m
            (Throw your hands up at me)
            Bm            F♯m  Bm
            All the la - dies         who truly feel me
            F♯m                      E  F♯m
            (Throw your hands up at me).
```

cont.

F♯m E F♯m
Girl I didn't know you could get down like that,
F♯m E F♯m
Charlie, how your An - gels get down like that,
F♯m E F♯m
Girl I didn't know you could get down like that,
F♯m E F♯m
Charlie, how your An - gels get down like that.

Verse 2

F♯m E F♯m
Tell me how you feel about this?
F♯m E F♯m
Who would I want if I would wan - na live?
F♯m E F♯m
I worked hard and sacrificed to get what I get,
F♯m E F♯m
Ladies, it ain't easy bein' in - depen - dent.
N.C. F♯m E F♯m
Question: How'd you like this know - ledge that I brought?
F♯m E F♯m
Braggin' on that cash that he gave you is the front,
F♯m E F♯m
If you're gonna brag make sure it's your money you flaunt,
F♯m E F♯m
Depend on no-one else to give you what you want.
Bm F♯m Bm
The shoes on my feet

(I've bought it)
F♯m E F♯m
The clothes I'm wear - ing

(I've bought it)
Bm F♯m Bm
The rock I'm rock - in'

(I've bought it)
F♯m E F♯m
'Cos I depend on me
Bm F♯m Bm
If I wanted the watch you're wear - in'

(I'll buy it)

```
              F♯m      E     F♯m
cont.         The house I live in

              (I've bought it)
                  Bm       F♯m   Bm
              The car I'm driv - ing

              (I've bought it)
              C♯sus4       C♯
              I depend on me

              (I depend on me).

              F♯m             E      F♯m
Chorus 2      All the wo - men who are independent
              F♯m                       E  F♯m
              (Throw your hands up at me)
              F♯m             E    F♯m
              All the hon - eys who makin' money
              F♯m                       E      F♯m
              (Throw your hands up at me)
              Bm                 F♯m  Bm
              All the mom - mas who profit dollas
              F♯m                       E  F♯m
              (Throw your hands up at me)
              Bm            F♯m  Bm
              All the la - dies  who truly feel me
              F♯m                       E  F♯m
              (Throw your hands up at me).
              F♯m                     E           F♯m
              Girl I didn't know you could get down like that,
              F♯m                           E         F♯m
              Charlie, how your An - gels get down like that,
              F♯m                     E           F♯m
              Girl I didn't know you could get down like that,
              F♯m                           E         F♯m
              Charlie, how your An - gels get down like that.
                          Bm
              Destiny's Child

              (Wassup?)
              F♯m        Bm
                 You in the house?

              (Sure 'nuff)
                    F♯m                          E    F♯m
              We'll break these people off        Angel style
```

```
              (F♯m)
Bridge        Child of Destiny,

              Independent beauty,
                        Bm
              No-one else can scare me,
                          F♯m
              Charlie's Angels

              Woah,

              Bm            F♯m Bm
Chorus 3      All the wo - men who independent
              C♯sus4                 C♯
              (Throw your hands up at me)
              F♯m           E   F♯m
              All the hon - eys who makin' money
              F♯m                   E   F♯m
              (Throw your hands up at me)
              F♯m            E    F♯m
              All the mom - mas who profit dollas
              F♯m                   E      F♯m
              (Throw your hands up at me)
              Bm           F♯m Bm
              All the la - dies who truly feel me
              F♯m                   E      F♯m
              (Throw your hands up at me)

                 Bm                    F♯m        Bm
Outro         ||: Girl I didn't know you could get down like that,
              F♯m                         E     F♯m
              Charlie, how your An - gels get down like that, :|| Repeat to fade
```

Think Twice

Words & Music by
Andy Hill & Pete Sinfield

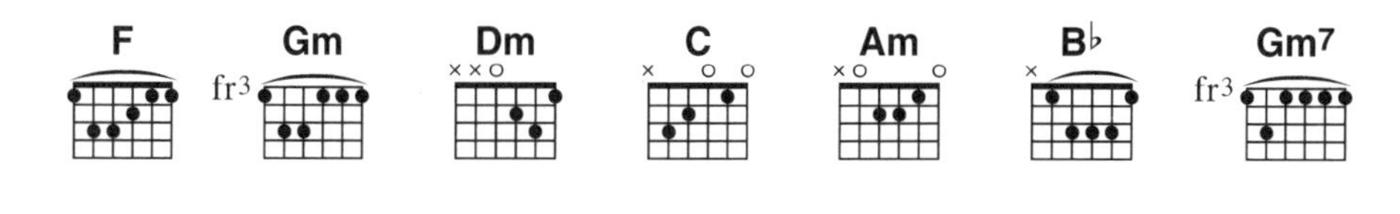

Intro | F | Gm | F | Gm ||

Verse 1

```
Dm                                    Gm
   Don't think I can't feel that there's something wrong,
C                                         Am        B♭
   You've been the sweetest part of my life for so long.
Dm                              Gm
   I look in your eyes, there's a distant light,
C                                   Am        B♭
   And you and I know there'll be a storm to - night.
Gm                 C
   This is getting serious,
Gm7                        C
   Are you thinking 'bout you or us?
```

Chorus 1

```
      F                       B♭      C
Don't say what you're a - bout to say,
     F                Am        B♭      C
Look back before you leave my life.
     F              B♭          C
Be sure before you close that door,
           Gm7       B♭
Before you roll those dice,
           F      Gm
Baby, think twice.
```

```
                    Dm                                Gm7
Verse 2      Baby think twice for the sake of our love, for the memory,
             C                                Am     B♭
               For the fire and the faith that was you and me.
             Dm                                          Gm7
               Babe I know it ain't easy when your soul cries out   for higher ground,
             C                                           Am     B♭
               'Cos when you're halfway up, you're always halfway down.
             Gm7             C              Gm7
               But baby this is serious, (this is serious.)
                                  C
             Are you thinking 'bout you or us?

                   F                 B♭     C
Chorus 2     Don't say what you're a - bout to say,
                  F               Am      B♭    C
             Look back before you leave my life.
                F              B♭       C
             Be sure before you close that door,
                         Gm7      B♭
             Before you roll those dice,
                         (Dm)
             Baby, think twice.

Guitar solo  | Dm      | Gm      | Dm      | Gm      ||

             Gm   B♭            C
Bridge                 Baby this is serious
             Gm   B♭                        C
                       Are you thinking about you or us?
             N.C.
             Baby.____
```

Chorus 3

(F) (B♭) (C) N.C.
Don't say what you're a - bout to say (no, no, no, no!)

F Am B♭ C
Look back before you leave my life (don't leave my life)

F B♭ C
Be sure before you close that door,

Gm7 B♭
Before you roll those dice__ (baby think twice.)

F B♭ C
Don't do what you're a - bout to do,

F Am B♭ C
My everything depends on you (I depend on you)

F B♭ C
And what - ever it takes, I'll sacri - fice,

Gm7 B♭
Before you roll those dice.

F B♭ C
Don't say what you're a - bout to say,

F Am B♭ C
Look back before you leave my life.

F B♭ C
Be sure before you close that door,

Gm7 B♭
Before you roll those dice,

F
Baby, think twice.

Fade

Suspicious Minds

Words & Music by
Francis Zambon

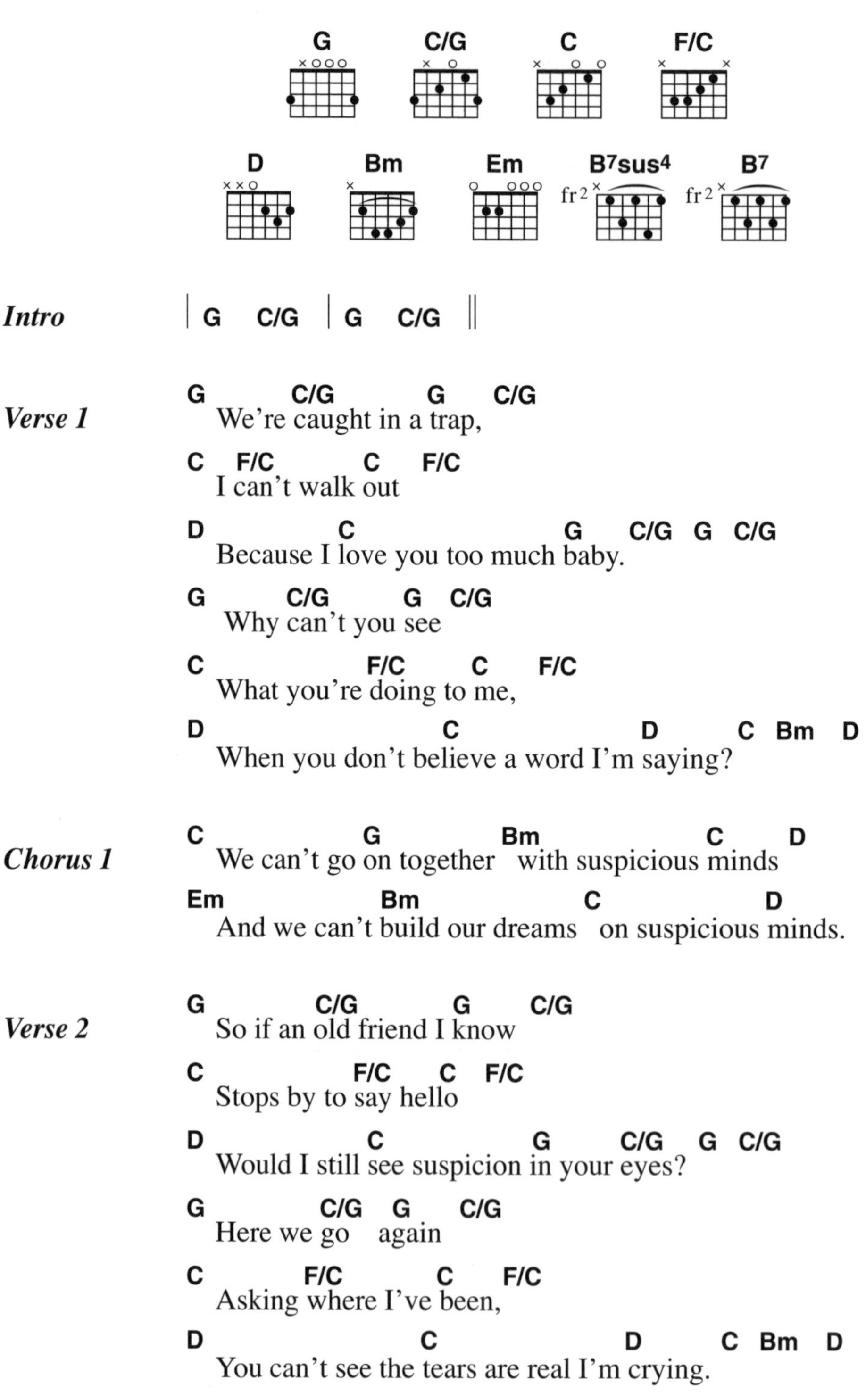

Intro | G C/G | G C/G ||

Verse 1

G C/G G C/G
We're caught in a trap,
C F/C C F/C
I can't walk out
D C G C/G G C/G
Because I love you too much baby.
G C/G G C/G
Why can't you see
C F/C C F/C
What you're doing to me,
D C D C Bm D
When you don't believe a word I'm saying?

Chorus 1

C G Bm C D
We can't go on together with suspicious minds
Em Bm C D
And we can't build our dreams on suspicious minds.

Verse 2

G C/G G C/G
So if an old friend I know
C F/C C F/C
Stops by to say hello
D C G C/G G C/G
Would I still see suspicion in your eyes?
G C/G G C/G
Here we go again
C F/C C F/C
Asking where I've been,
D C D C Bm D
You can't see the tears are real I'm crying.

Chorus 2

C G Bm C D
We can't go on together with suspicious minds

Em Bm C B7sus4 B7
And we can't build our dreams on suspicious minds.

Bridge

Em Bm C D
Oh let our love survive, I'll dry the tears from your eyes

Em Bm
Let's don't let a good thing die

C D G C
When honey, you know I've never lied to you, hmmm-mmm,

G D
Yeah, yeah.

Verse 3

G C/G G C/G
We're caught in a trap,

C F/C C F/C
I can't walk out

D C G C/G G C/G
Because I love you too much baby.

G C/G G C/G
Why can't you see

C F/C C F/C
What you're doing to me,

D C G C/G G C/G
When you don't believe a word I'm saying.

Ah don't you know...

Verse 4

𝄆 As Verse 3 𝄇 *Repeat to fade*

Like A Rolling Stone

Words & Music by
Bob Dylan

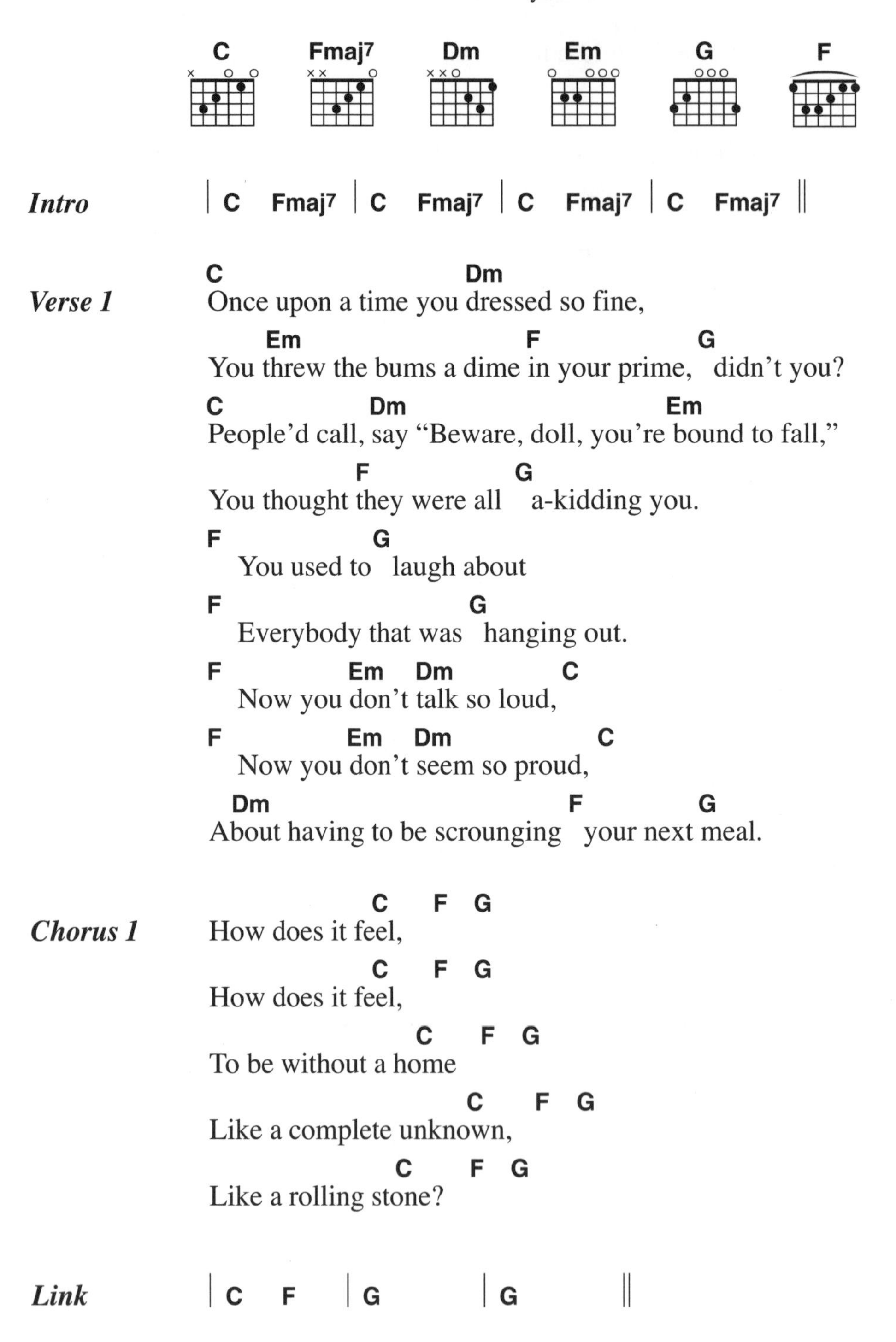

Intro | C Fmaj7 | C Fmaj7 | C Fmaj7 | C Fmaj7 ||

Verse 1

```
C                          Dm
Once upon a time you dressed so fine,
      Em                          F              G
You threw the bums a dime in your prime,   didn't you?
C               Dm                          Em
People'd call, say "Beware, doll, you're bound to fall,"
                F                 G
You thought they were all    a-kidding you.
F              G
   You used to    laugh about
F                       G
   Everybody that was    hanging out.
F              Em    Dm            C
   Now you don't talk so loud,
F              Em    Dm                C
   Now you don't seem so proud,
  Dm                                  F           G
About having to be scrounging    your next meal.
```

Chorus 1

```
                C     F    G
How does it feel,
                C     F    G
How does it feel,
                    C     F    G
To be without a home
                         C     F    G
Like a complete unknown,
                    C     F    G
Like a rolling stone?
```

Link | C F | G | G ||

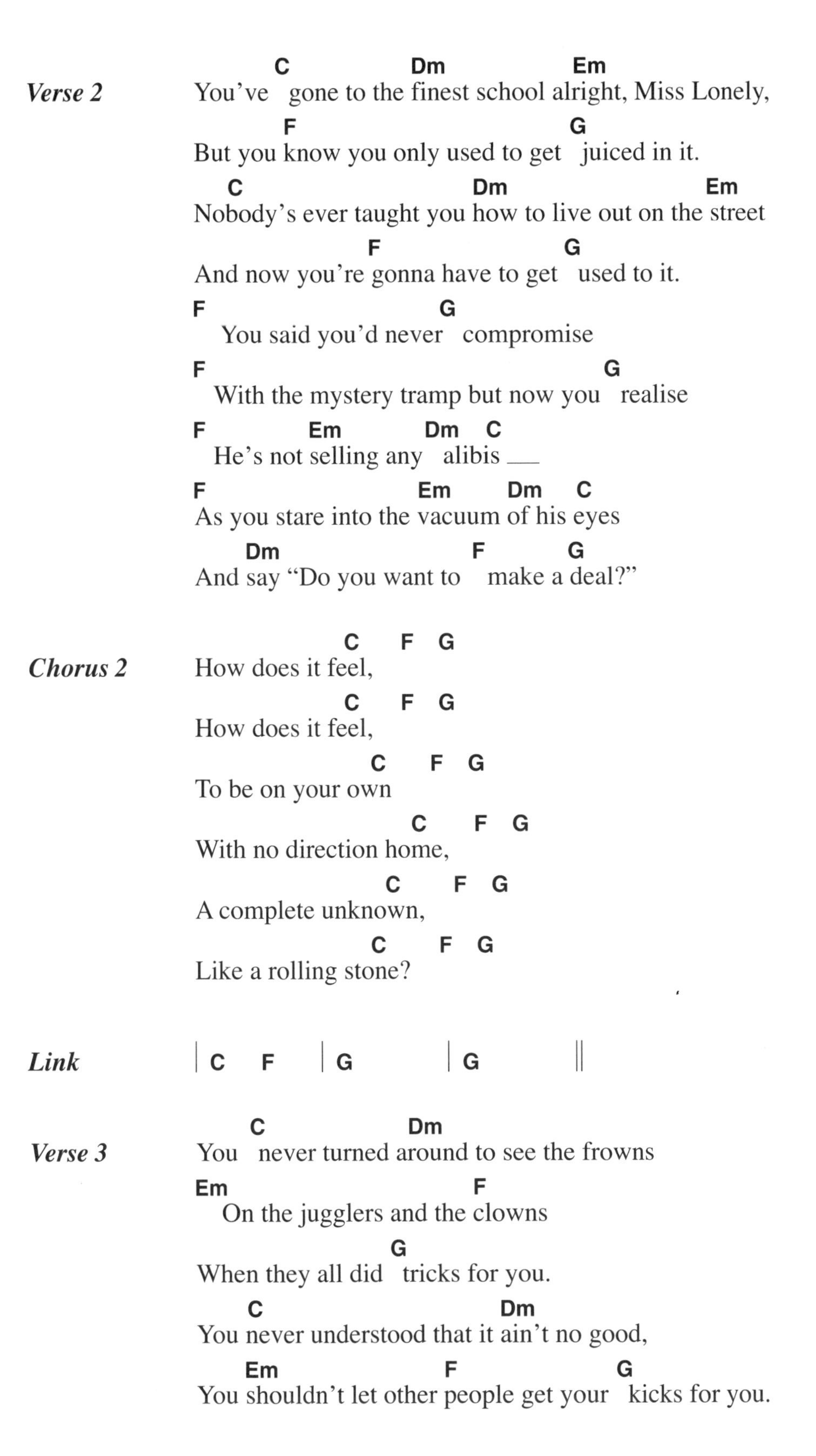

Verse 2

C Dm Em
You've gone to the finest school alright, Miss Lonely,
F G
But you know you only used to get juiced in it.
C Dm Em
Nobody's ever taught you how to live out on the street
F G
And now you're gonna have to get used to it.
F G
You said you'd never compromise
F G
With the mystery tramp but now you realise
F Em Dm C
He's not selling any alibis ___
F Em Dm C
As you stare into the vacuum of his eyes
Dm F G
And say "Do you want to make a deal?"

Chorus 2

C F G
How does it feel,
C F G
How does it feel,
C F G
To be on your own
C F G
With no direction home,
C F G
A complete unknown,
C F G
Like a rolling stone?

Link

| C F | G | G ||

Verse 3

C Dm
You never turned around to see the frowns
Em F
On the jugglers and the clowns
G
When they all did tricks for you.
C Dm
You never understood that it ain't no good,
Em F G
You shouldn't let other people get your kicks for you.

cont.

```
F                                                   G
   You used to ride on the chrome horse with your  diplomat
F                               G
   Who carried on his shoulder a  Siamese cat.
F             Em          Dm      C
   Ain't it hard  when you discover that
F           Em    Dm       C
   He really wasn't where it's at
Dm
After he took from you everything
F          G
   He could steal? __
```

Chorus 3

```
                  C    F  G
How does it feel,
                  C    F  G
How does it feel,
                    C    F  G
To be on your own
                       C    F  G
With no direction home,
                         C    F  G
Like a complete unknown,
                    C    F  G
Like a rolling stone?
```

Link

```
| C   F  | G        | G        ||
```

Verse 4

```
C               Dm                 Em
   Princess on the steeple and all the  pretty people
               F                       G
They're all drinking, thinking that they  got it made,
C              Dm
   Exchanging all  precious gifts
Em                 F
   But you'd better take your diamond ring,
G
   You'd better pawn it babe.
F              G
   You used to be  so amused
F                        G
   At Napoleon in rags  and the language that he used.
```

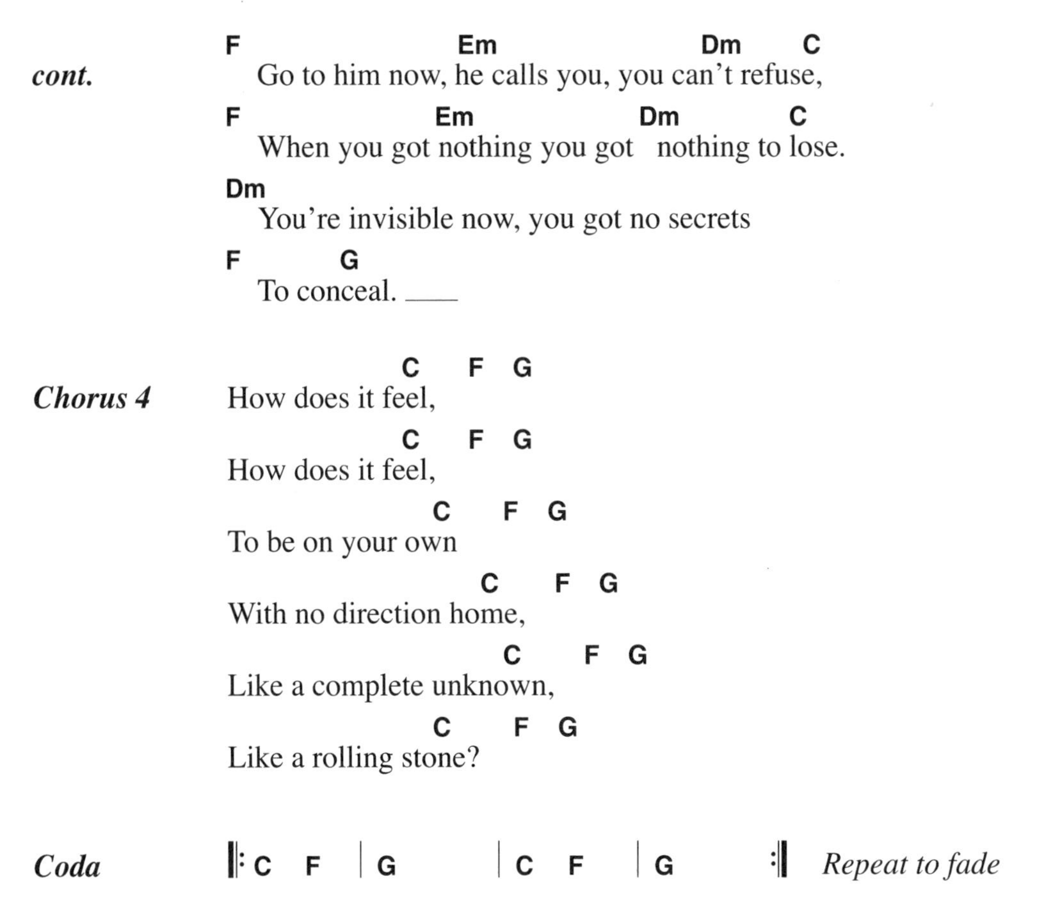

```
cont.       F                  Em                   Dm      C
              Go to him now, he calls you, you can't refuse,
            F                Em                 Dm          C
              When you got nothing you got   nothing to lose.
            Dm
              You're invisible now, you got no secrets
            F         G
              To conceal. ___

                         C    F   G
Chorus 4    How does it feel,
                         C    F   G
            How does it feel,
                           C     F   G
            To be on your own
                              C     F   G
            With no direction home,
                               C     F   G
            Like a complete unknown,
                           C     F   G
            Like a rolling stone?

Coda        ||: C   F  | G        | C   F  | G        :||  Repeat to fade
```

Respect

Words & Music by
Otis Redding

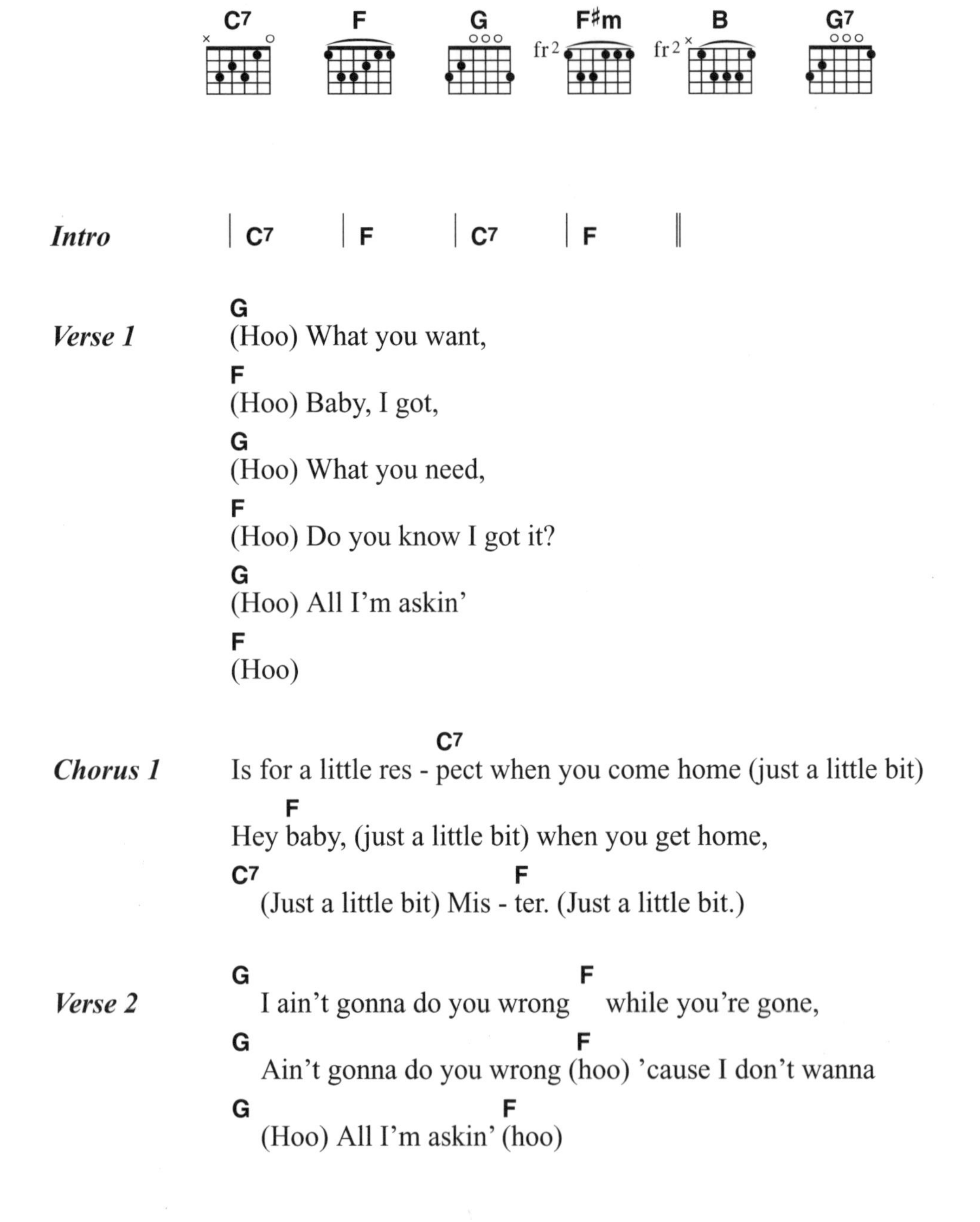

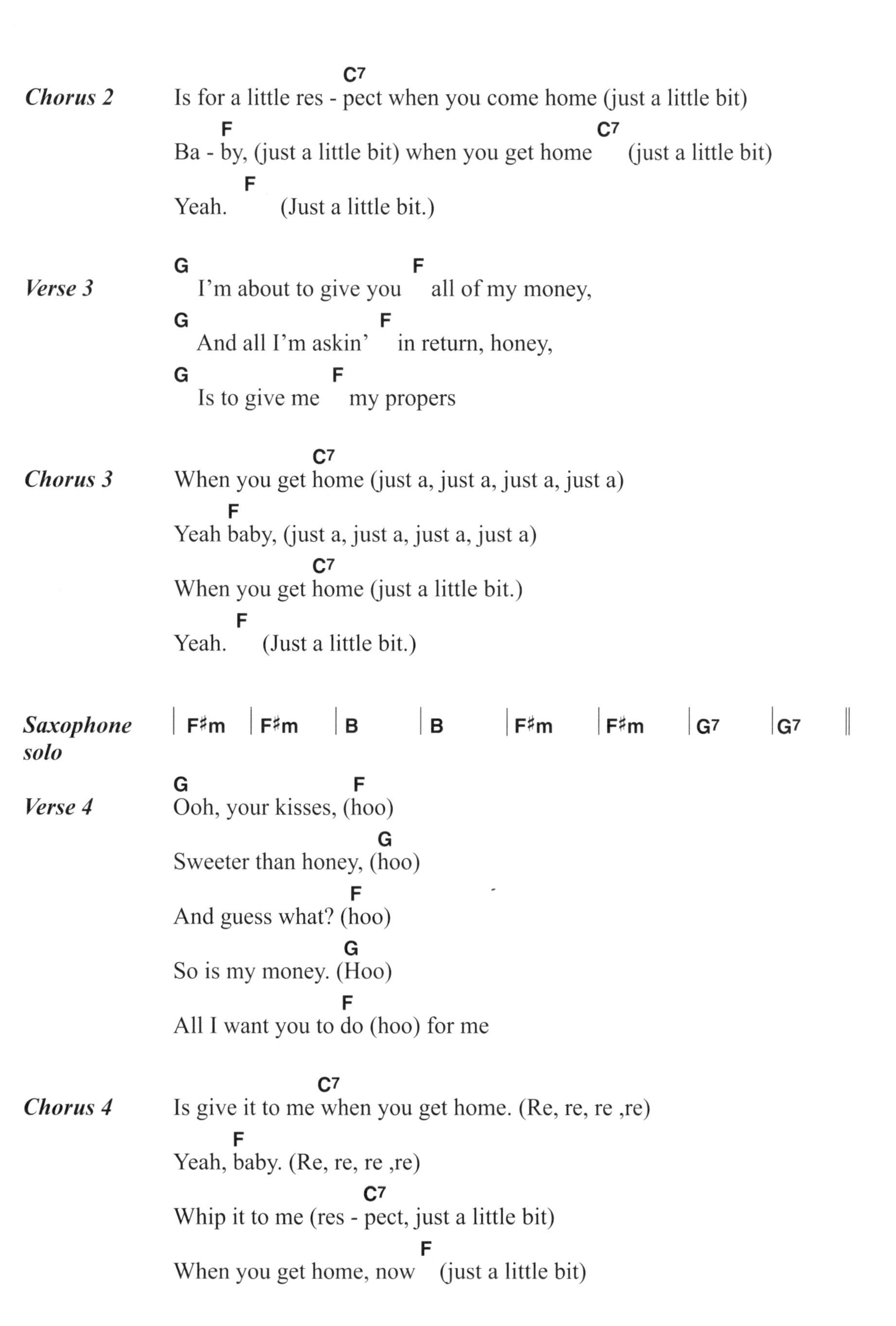

Chorus 2

C7
Is for a little res - pect when you come home (just a little bit)
F C7
Ba - by, (just a little bit) when you get home (just a little bit)
F
Yeah. (Just a little bit.)

Verse 3

G F
I'm about to give you all of my money,
G F
And all I'm askin' in return, honey,
G F
Is to give me my propers

Chorus 3

C7
When you get home (just a, just a, just a, just a)
F
Yeah baby, (just a, just a, just a, just a)
C7
When you get home (just a little bit.)
F
Yeah. (Just a little bit.)

Saxophone solo

| F♯m | F♯m | B | B | F♯m | F♯m | G7 | G7 ||

Verse 4

G F
Ooh, your kisses, (hoo)
G
Sweeter than honey, (hoo)
F
And guess what? (hoo)
G
So is my money. (Hoo)
F
All I want you to do (hoo) for me

Chorus 4

C7
Is give it to me when you get home. (Re, re, re ,re)
F
Yeah, baby. (Re, re, re ,re)
C7
Whip it to me (res - pect, just a little bit)
F
When you get home, now (just a little bit)

Middle

C7 N.C.
R-E-S-P-E-C-T

F N.C.
Find out what it means to me

C7 N.C.
R-E-S-P-E-C-T

F N.C.
Take care, TCB

Chorus 5

C7
Oh (sock it to me, sock it to me,

Sock it to me, sock it to me)

F
A little res - pect (sock it to me, sock it to me,

Sock it to me, sock it to me)

C7
Whoa, babe (just a little bit)

F
A little res - pect (just a little bit)

C7
I get tired (just a little bit)

F
Keep on tryin' (just a little bit)

C7
You're runnin' out of foolin' (just a little bit)

F
And I ain't lyin' (just a little bit)

C7
(Re, re, re, re) 'spect

F
When you come home (re, re, re ,re)

C7
Or you might walk in (respect, just a little bit)

F
And find out I'm gone (just a little bit)...

Fade

Sexual Healing

Words & Music by
Marvin Gaye, Odell Brown & David Ritz

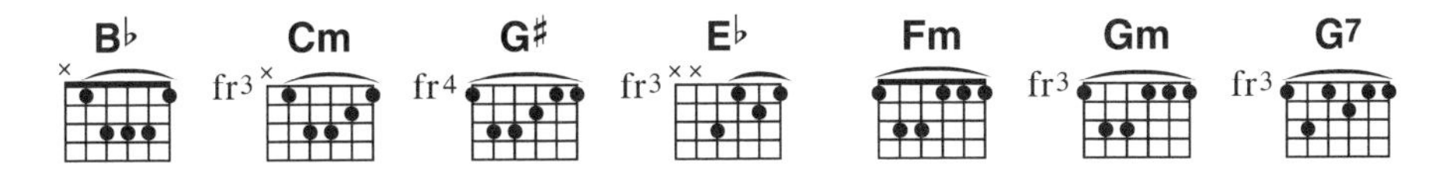

Intro

N.C.
Get up, get up, get up, get up.

Wake up, wake up, wake up, wake up.
B♭ Cm G♯ E♭
Oh baby, now let's get down tonight.

| B♭ | Cm | G♯ | E♭ |

Verse 1

B♭ Cm G♯ E♭ B♭ Cm
Ooh ba - by, I'm hot just like an oven,
G♯ E♭
I need some lovin'.
B♭ Cm G♯ E♭ B♭ Cm
And ba - by, I can't hold it much longer,
G♯ E♭
It's getting stronger and stronger.

Chorus 1

B♭ Cm
And when I get that feeling
G♯ E♭
I want sexual healing
B♭ Cm G♯ E♭
Sexual healing, oh baby.
B♭ Cm G♯ E♭
Makes me feel so fine,
B♭ Cm G♯ E♭
Helps to relieve my mind,
B♭ Cm G♯ E♭
Sexual healing baby, is good for me,
B♭ Cm Fm Gm G♯ B♭ E♭
Sexual healing is something that's good for me.

Bridge 1

E♭ G7
Whenever blue teardrops are falling
G♯ Fm Gm G♯ B♭
And my emotional sta - bility is leav - ing me,
E♭ G7
There is something I can do
G♯ Fm Gm G♯ B♭
I can get on the telephone and call you up baby, and
E♭ G7
Honey I know you'll be there to relieve me
G♯ Fm Gm G♯ B♭
The love you give to me will free me
E♭ G7
If you don't know the things you're dealing
G♯ Fm Gm G♯ B♭
Oh, I can tell you, darling, that it's sexual healing.
B♭ Cm G♯ E♭
Get up, get up, get up, get up, let's make love tonight,
B♭ Cm G♯ E♭
Wake up, wake up, wake up, wake up, 'cos you do it right.

Verse 2

B♭ Cm G♯ E♭ B♭ Cm
Ba - by, I got sick this morning,
G♯ E♭
A sea was storming inside of me.
B♭ Cm G♯ E♭ B♭ Cm
Ba - by, I think I'm cap - sizing,
G♯ E♭
The waves are rising and rising.

Chorus 2

B♭ Cm
And when I get that feeling
G♯ E♭
I want sexual healing
B♭ Cm G♯ E♭
Sexual healing is good for me
B♭ Cm G♯ E♭
Makes me feel so fine, it's such a rush
B♭ Cm G♯ E♭
Helps to relieve the mind, and it's good for us.
B♭ Cm G♯ E♭
Sexual healing, baby, is good for me
B♭ Cm Fm Gm G♯ B♭ E♭
Sexual healing is something that's good for me.

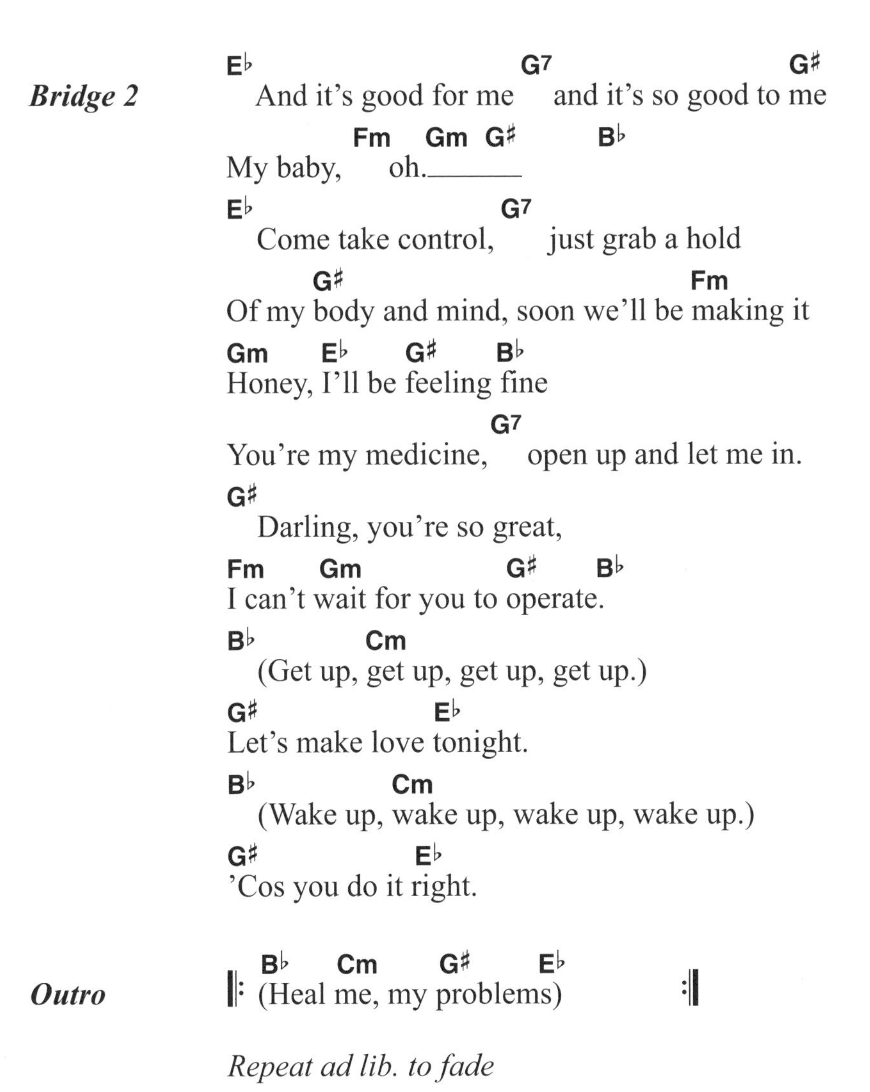

Bridge 2

E♭ G7 G♯
And it's good for me and it's so good to me
Fm Gm G♯ B♭
My baby, oh.______
E♭ G7
Come take control, just grab a hold
G♯ Fm
Of my body and mind, soon we'll be making it
Gm E♭ G♯ B♭
Honey, I'll be feeling fine
G7
You're my medicine, open up and let me in.
G♯
Darling, you're so great,
Fm Gm G♯ B♭
I can't wait for you to operate.
B♭ Cm
(Get up, get up, get up, get up.)
G♯ E♭
Let's make love tonight.
B♭ Cm
(Wake up, wake up, wake up, wake up.)
G♯ E♭
'Cos you do it right.

Outro

B♭ Cm G♯ E♭
𝄆 (Heal me, my problems) 𝄇

Repeat ad lib. to fade

(Sittin' On) The Dock Of The Bay

Words & Music by
Steve Cropper & Otis Redding

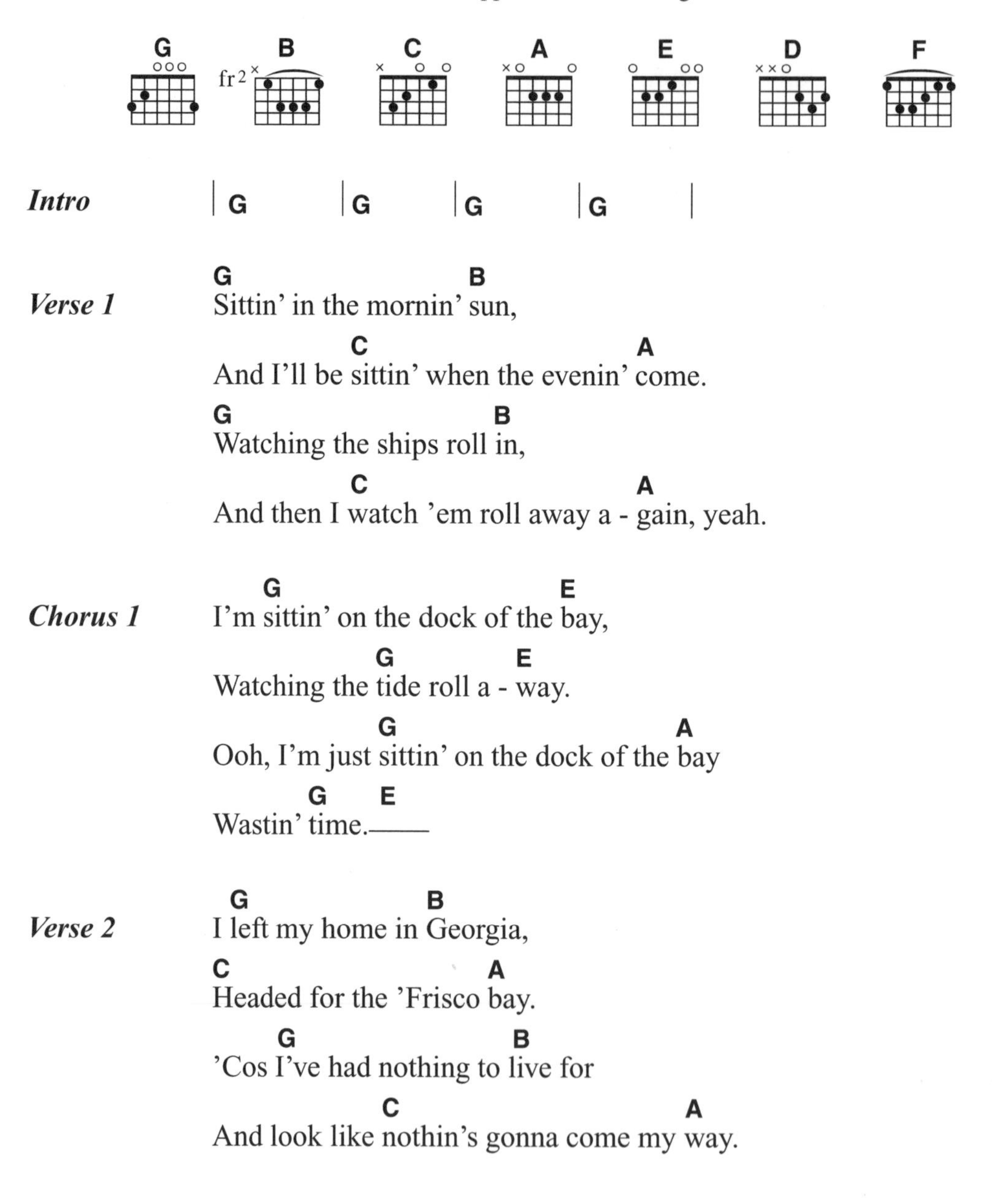


```
Intro       | G      | G      | G      | G      |

            G                B
Verse 1     Sittin' in the mornin' sun,
                           C                     A
            And I'll be sittin' when the evenin' come.
            G                        B
            Watching the ships roll in,
                           C                     A
            And then I watch 'em roll away a - gain, yeah.

                 G                         E
Chorus 1    I'm sittin' on the dock of the bay,
                               G          E
            Watching the tide roll a - way.
                               G                       A
            Ooh, I'm just sittin' on the dock of the bay
                      G   E
            Wastin' time.___

              G                B
Verse 2     I left my home in Georgia,
            C                        A
            Headed for the 'Frisco bay.
                  G                  B
            'Cos I've had nothing to live for
                               C                      A
            And look like nothin's gonna come my way.
```

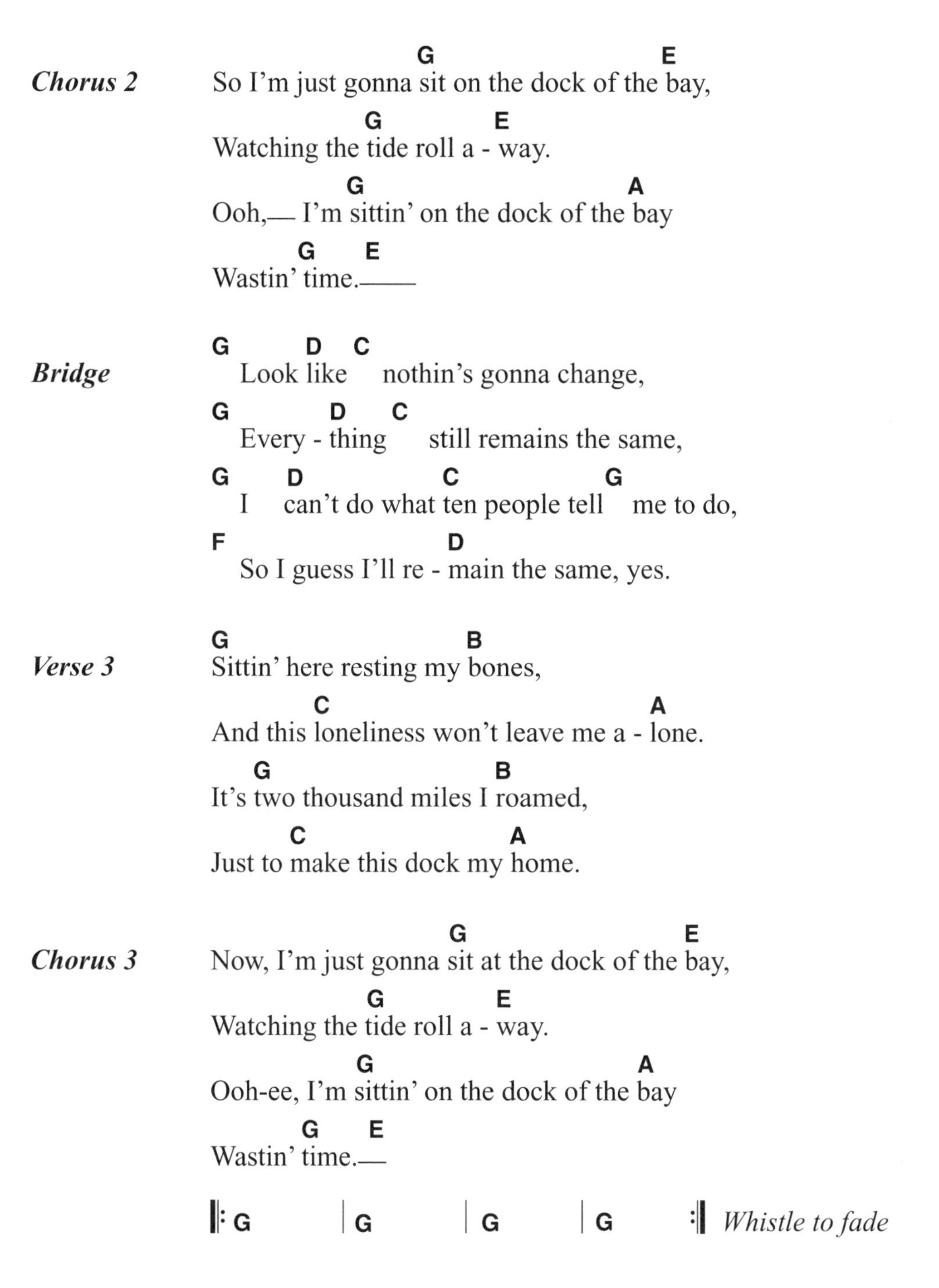

Chorus 2
G E
So I'm just gonna sit on the dock of the bay,
G E
Watching the tide roll a - way.
G A
Ooh,— I'm sittin' on the dock of the bay
G E
Wastin' time.——
Bridge
G D C
Look like nothin's gonna change,
G D C
Every - thing still remains the same,
G D C G
I can't do what ten people tell me to do,
F D
So I guess I'll re - main the same, yes.
Verse 3
G B
Sittin' here resting my bones,
C A
And this loneliness won't leave me a - lone.
G B
It's two thousand miles I roamed,
C A
Just to make this dock my home.
Chorus 3
G E
Now, I'm just gonna sit at the dock of the bay,
G E
Watching the tide roll a - way.
G A
Ooh-ee, I'm sittin' on the dock of the bay
G E
Wastin' time.—
G | G | G | G
Whistle to fade

Living In America

Words & Music by
Dan Hartman & Charlie Midnight

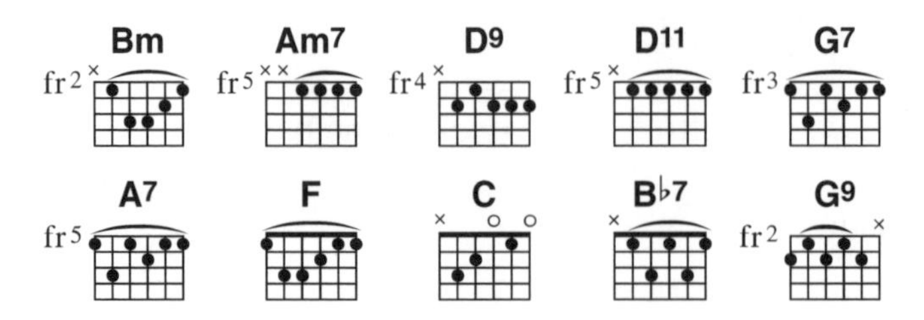

Intro

Bm
Yeah, ugh!
Am7
Get up, now!

Bm Am7
D9 | D9 | D9 | D9 |
Ow!
D9 | D9 | D9 | D9 | D9
Knock it out, yeah!

Verse 1

D9 D11 D9 D11 D9 D11
Yeah! Sup - er highways, coast to coast, easy to get
D9 D11
anywhere
D9 D11 D9 D11 D9 D11
On the trans - conti - nental overload, just slide behind the wheel,
D9 D11
How does it feel?
G7 D9 D11
When there's no destination, that's too far,
G7 A7
And somewhere on the way, you might find out who you are.

Chorus 1

F G7
(Living in America)
D9 D11 D9 D11
Eye to eye, sta - tion to station,
F G7
(Living in America)
D9 D11 D9 D11
Hand to hand, across the nation,
F C
(Living in America)
B♭7 D9
Got to have a celebration.
D9 D11
Rock my soul, huh!
D9 D11
Aw!
D9 D11
Huh!

D9 D11

Verse 2

D9 D11 D9 D11 D9 D11 D11
Smoke - stack, fat - back, many miles of railroad track,
D9 D11 D9 D11 D9 D11 D9 D11
All night ra - dio, keep on runnin' through your rock 'n' roll soul.
D9 D11 D9 D11
All night diners keep you awake, hey,
D9 D11 D9 D11
On black coffee and a hard roll, woah!
G7
(But you might have to walk the fine line.) Say?
G7
(You might take the hard line.)
G7 A7
But everybody's working overtime.

Chorus 2

F G7
(Living in America)
D9 D11 D9 D11
Eye to eye, sta - tion to station,
F G7
(Living in America)
D9 D11 D9 D11
Hand to hand, across the nation.
F C
(Living in America)

cont.

```
B♭7                          D9
Got to have a celebration,     roaw!
 D9  D11          D9    D11
I      live in Am - erica,
D9  D11  D9               D11
           Help me out.
 D9   D11            D9    D11
I       live in Am - erica,
D9    D11                     D9     D11
            Wait a minute!
```

Bridge

```
Bm
   You may not be looking for the promised land,

But you might find it anyway.
G9
   Under one of those old familiar names,
      D9
Like New Orleans (New Orleans),

Detroit City (Detroit City),

Dallas (Dallas)

Pittsburg P.A. (Pittsburg P.A.),

New York City (New York City)

Kansas City (Kansas City), Atlanta (Atlanta),

Chicago and L.A.
```

Chorus 3

```
F                   G7
(Living in America)
D9    D11    D9 D11
                  Hit me!
F                   G7
(Living in America)
               D9  D11      D9   D11
Yeah, I walk in       and out.
F                   G7
(Living in America)
B♭7
    Woah!
```

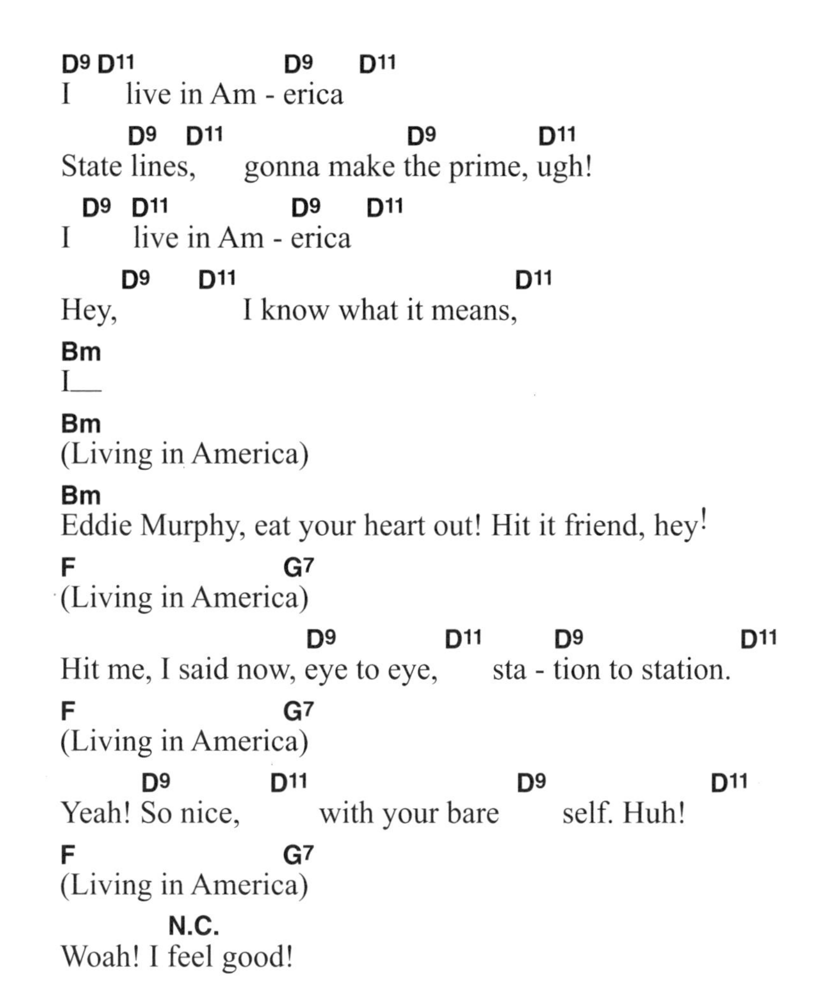
cont.
D9 D11 D9 D11
I live in Am - erica
D9 D11 D9 D11
State lines, gonna make the prime, ugh!
D9 D11 D9 D11
I live in Am - erica
D9 D11 D11
Hey, I know what it means,
Bm
I__
Bm
(Living in America)
Bm
Eddie Murphy, eat your heart out! Hit it friend, hey!
F G7
(Living in America)
D9 D11 D9 D11
Hit me, I said now, eye to eye, sta - tion to station.
F G7
(Living in America)
D9 D11 D9 D11
Yeah! So nice, with your bare self. Huh!
F G7
(Living in America)
N.C.
Woah! I feel good!

Oh, Pretty Woman

Words & Music by
Roy Orbison & Bill Dees

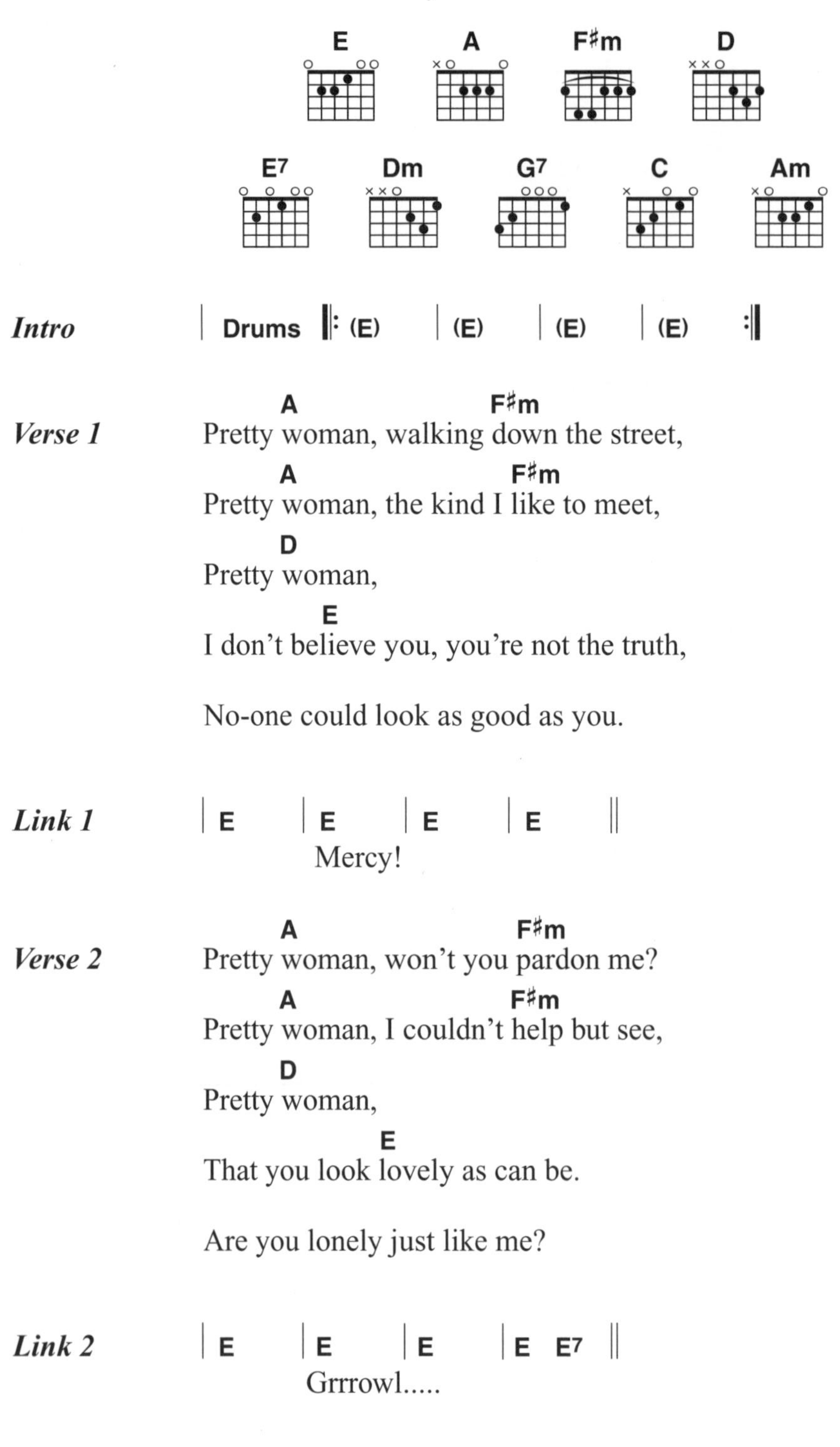

Intro | Drums |: (E) | (E) | (E) | (E) :|

Verse 1

```
            A                    F♯m
Pretty woman, walking down the street,
            A                    F♯m
Pretty woman, the kind I like to meet,
            D
Pretty woman,
                  E
I don't believe you, you're not the truth,

No-one could look as good as you.
```

Link 1 | E | E | E | E ||

Mercy!

Verse 2

```
            A                      F♯m
Pretty woman, won't you pardon me?
            A                    F♯m
Pretty woman, I couldn't help but see,
            D
Pretty woman,
                       E
That you look lovely as can be.

Are you lonely just like me?
```

Link 2 | E | E | E | E E7 ||

Grrrowl.....

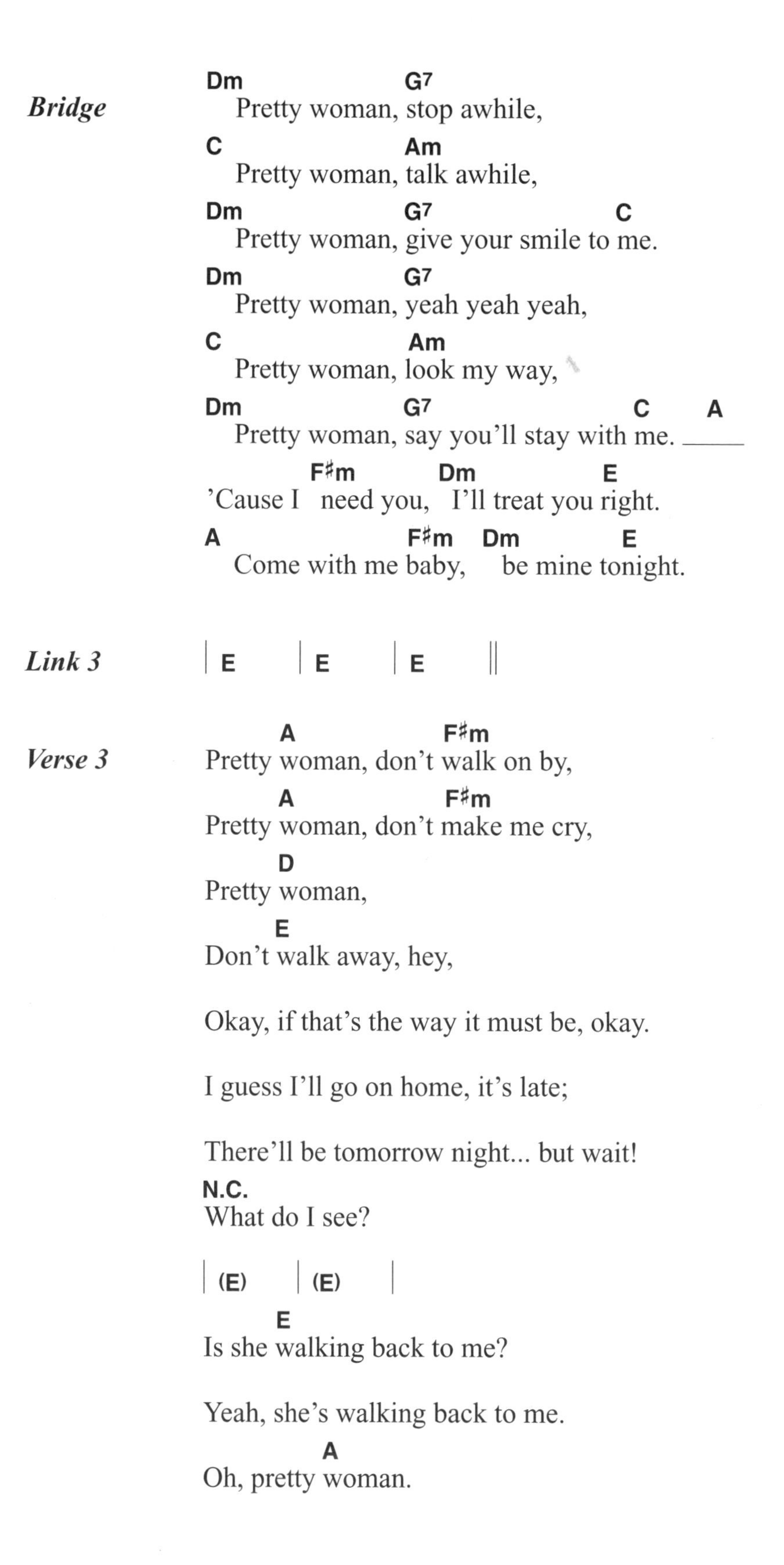

Bridge

Dm G7
Pretty woman, stop awhile,
C Am
Pretty woman, talk awhile,
Dm G7 C
Pretty woman, give your smile to me.
Dm G7
Pretty woman, yeah yeah yeah,
C Am
Pretty woman, look my way,
Dm G7 C A
Pretty woman, say you'll stay with me. ____
F♯m Dm E
'Cause I need you, I'll treat you right.
A F♯m Dm E
Come with me baby, be mine tonight.

Link 3

| E | E | E ||

Verse 3

A F♯m
Pretty woman, don't walk on by,
A F♯m
Pretty woman, don't make me cry,
D
Pretty woman,
E
Don't walk away, hey,

Okay, if that's the way it must be, okay.

I guess I'll go on home, it's late;

There'll be tomorrow night... but wait!
N.C.
What do I see?

| (E) | (E) |

E
Is she walking back to me?

Yeah, she's walking back to me.
A
Oh, pretty woman.

Mr. Tambourine Man

Words & Music by
Bob Dylan

D G/B A Em

Capo third fret, sixth string tuned down a tone

Intro | D | D ||

Chorus 1

G/B A D G/B
Hey! Mr. Tambourine Man, play a song for me,
D G/B A
I'm not sleepy and there is no place I'm going to.
G/B A D G/B
Hey! Mr. Tambourine Man, play a song for me,
D G/B A D
In the jingle jangle morning I'll come followin' you.

Verse 1

G/B A D G/B
Though I know that evenin's empire has returned into sand,
D G/B
Vanished from my hand,
D G/B Em A
Left me blindly here to stand but still not sleeping.
G/B A D G/B
My weariness amazes me, I'm branded on my feet,
D G/B
I have no one to meet,
D G/B Em A
And the ancient empty street's too dead for dreaming.

Chorus 2 As Chorus 1

Link 1 | D | D ||

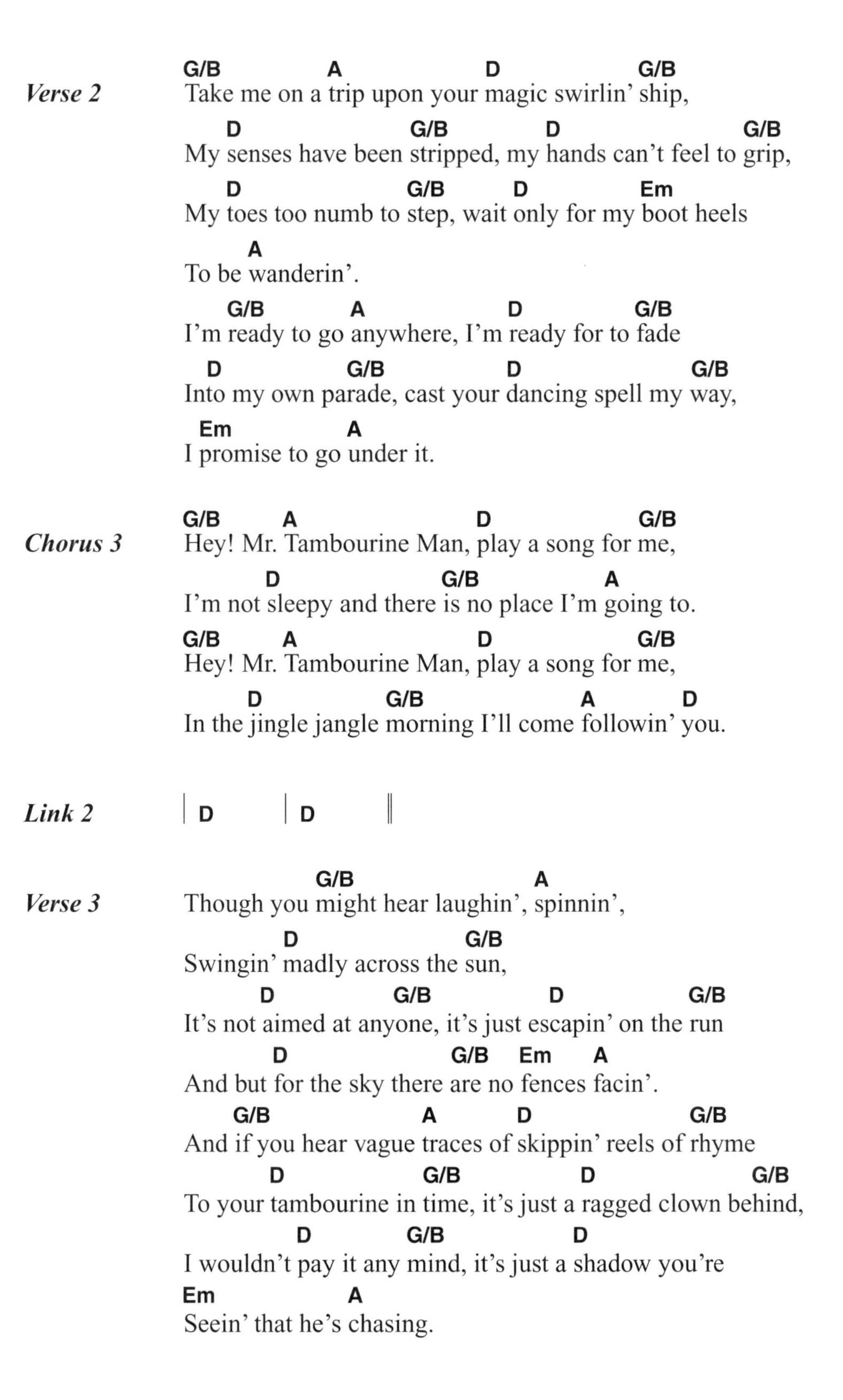

Verse 2

```
G/B          A                D             G/B
Take me on a trip upon your magic swirlin' ship,
   D                G/B          D                  G/B
My senses have been stripped, my hands can't feel to grip,
   D               G/B        D          Em
My toes too numb to step, wait only for my boot heels
     A
To be wanderin'.
   G/B           A               D           G/B
I'm ready to go anywhere, I'm ready for to fade
  D             G/B             D                 G/B
Into my own parade, cast your dancing spell my way,
  Em           A
I promise to go under it.
```

Chorus 3

```
G/B       A                  D            G/B
Hey! Mr. Tambourine Man, play a song for me,
      D            G/B          A
I'm not sleepy and there is no place I'm going to.
G/B       A                  D            G/B
Hey! Mr. Tambourine Man, play a song for me,
     D            G/B            A        D
In the jingle jangle morning I'll come followin' you.
```

Link 2

```
| D      | D      ||
```

Verse 3

```
                 G/B                A
Though you might hear laughin', spinnin',
          D             G/B
Swingin' madly across the sun,
       D             G/B             D            G/B
It's not aimed at anyone, it's just escapin' on the run
        D                  G/B   Em    A
And but for the sky there are no fences facin'.
    G/B              A       D              G/B
And if you hear vague traces of skippin' reels of rhyme
         D             G/B              D              G/B
To your tambourine in time, it's just a ragged clown behind,
           D         G/B                D
I wouldn't pay it any mind, it's just a shadow you're
Em            A
Seein' that he's chasing.
```

Chorus 4 As Chorus 3

Harmonica Break

```
| G/B  A | D  G/B | D  G/B | D  G/B | D  G/B |

| D  G/B | D  Em  | A      | G/B  A | D  G/B |

| D  G/B | D  G/B | D  Em  | A   D  | D      ||
```

Verse 4

```
     G/B         A                    D                 G/B
Then take me disappearin' through the smoke rings of my mind,
         D              G/B       D               G/B
Down the foggy ruins of time, far past the frozen leaves,
    D                   G/B        D            G/B
The haunted, frightened trees, out to the windy beach,
    D                G/B      Em    A
Far from the twisted reach of crazy sorrow.
        G/B               A                D
Yes, to dance beneath the diamond sky with one hand waving free,
        D          G/B          D             G/B
Silhouetted by the sea, circled by the circus sands,
         D          G/B         D                G/B
With all memory and fate driven deep beneath the waves,
          D         Em            A
Let me forget about today until tomorrow.
```

Chorus 5 As Chorus 3

Coda

Fade

```
| G/B  A | D  G/B | D  G/B | D  G/B | D  G/B ||
```

Going Underground

Words & Music by
Paul Weller

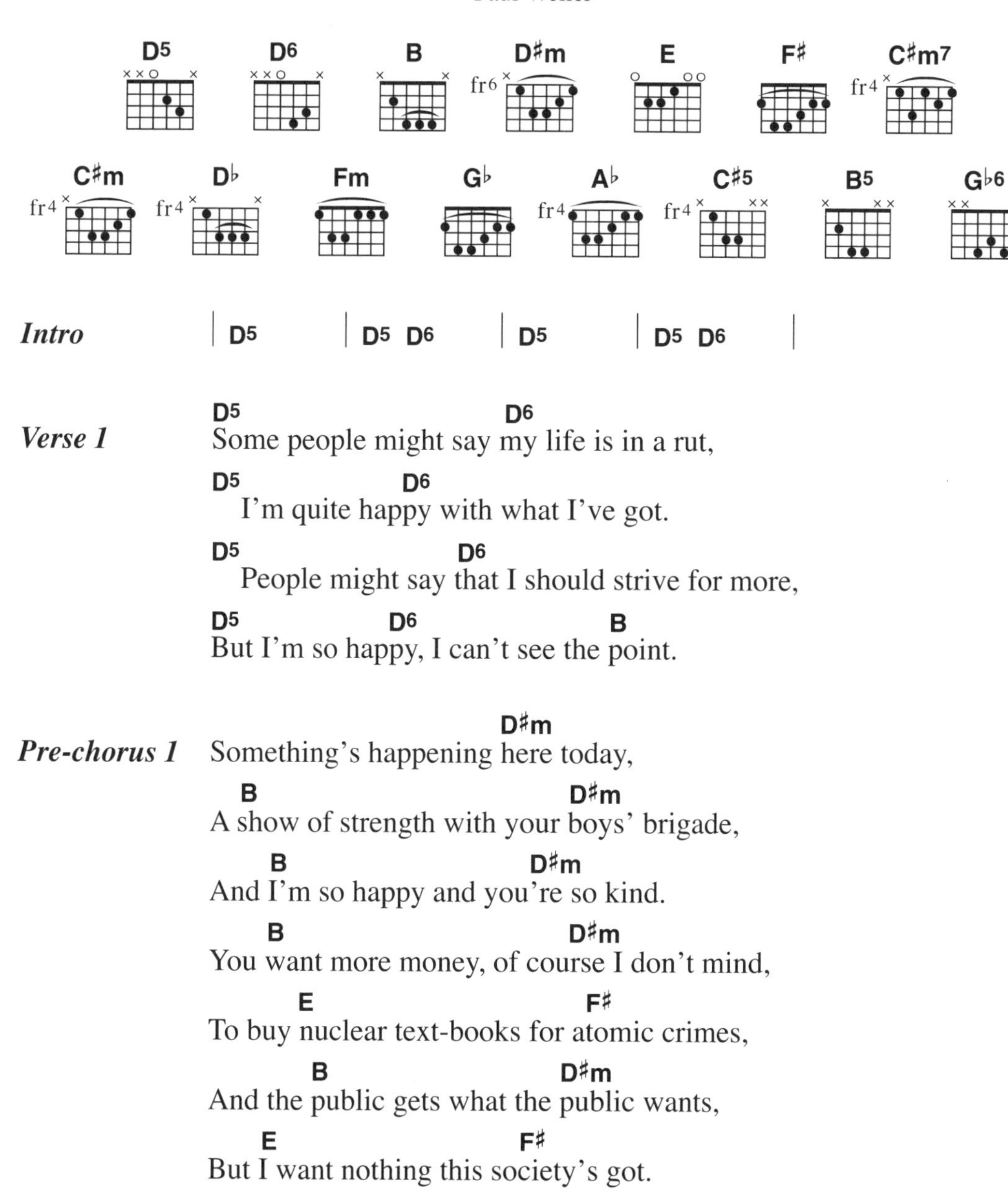

Intro | D5 | D5 D6 | D5 | D5 D6 |

Verse 1

D5 D6
Some people might say my life is in a rut,
D5 D6
I'm quite happy with what I've got.
D5 D6
People might say that I should strive for more,
D5 D6 B
But I'm so happy, I can't see the point.

Pre-chorus 1

D♯m
Something's happening here today,
B D♯m
A show of strength with your boys' brigade,
B D♯m
And I'm so happy and you're so kind.
B D♯m
You want more money, of course I don't mind,
E F♯
To buy nuclear text-books for atomic crimes,
B D♯m
And the public gets what the public wants,
E F♯
But I want nothing this society's got.

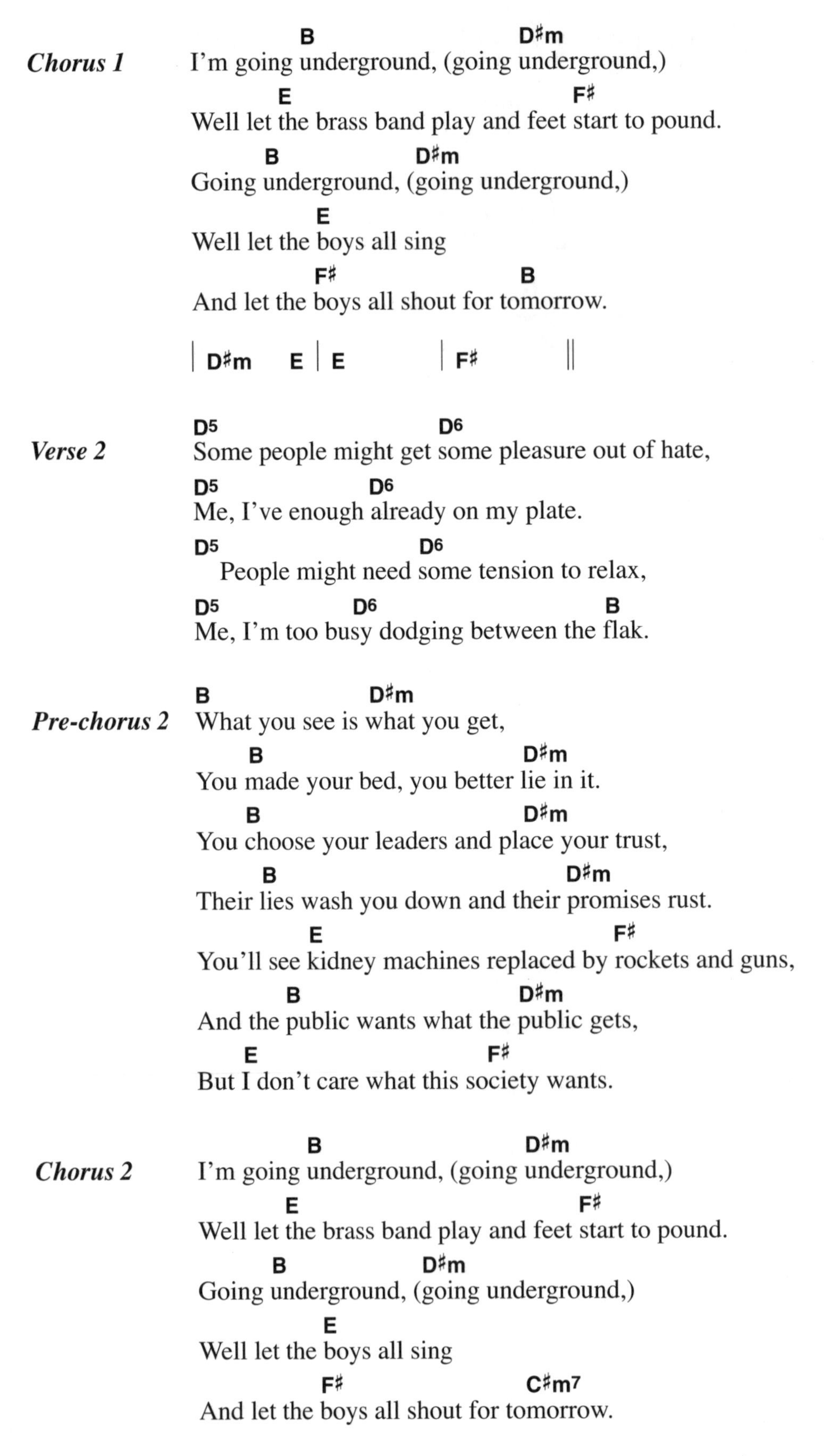

Chorus 1

B D♯m
I'm going underground, (going underground,)

E F♯
Well let the brass band play and feet start to pound.

B D♯m
Going underground, (going underground,)

E
Well let the boys all sing

F♯ B
And let the boys all shout for tomorrow.

| D♯m E | E | F♯ ||

Verse 2

D5 D6
Some people might get some pleasure out of hate,

D5 D6
Me, I've enough already on my plate.

D5 D6
People might need some tension to relax,

D5 D6 B
Me, I'm too busy dodging between the flak.

Pre-chorus 2

B D♯m
What you see is what you get,

B D♯m
You made your bed, you better lie in it.

B D♯m
You choose your leaders and place your trust,

B D♯m
Their lies wash you down and their promises rust.

E F♯
You'll see kidney machines replaced by rockets and guns,

B D♯m
And the public wants what the public gets,

E F♯
But I don't care what this society wants.

Chorus 2

B D♯m
I'm going underground, (going underground,)

E F♯
Well let the brass band play and feet start to pound.

B D♯m
Going underground, (going underground,)

E
Well let the boys all sing

F♯ C♯m7
And let the boys all shout for tomorrow.

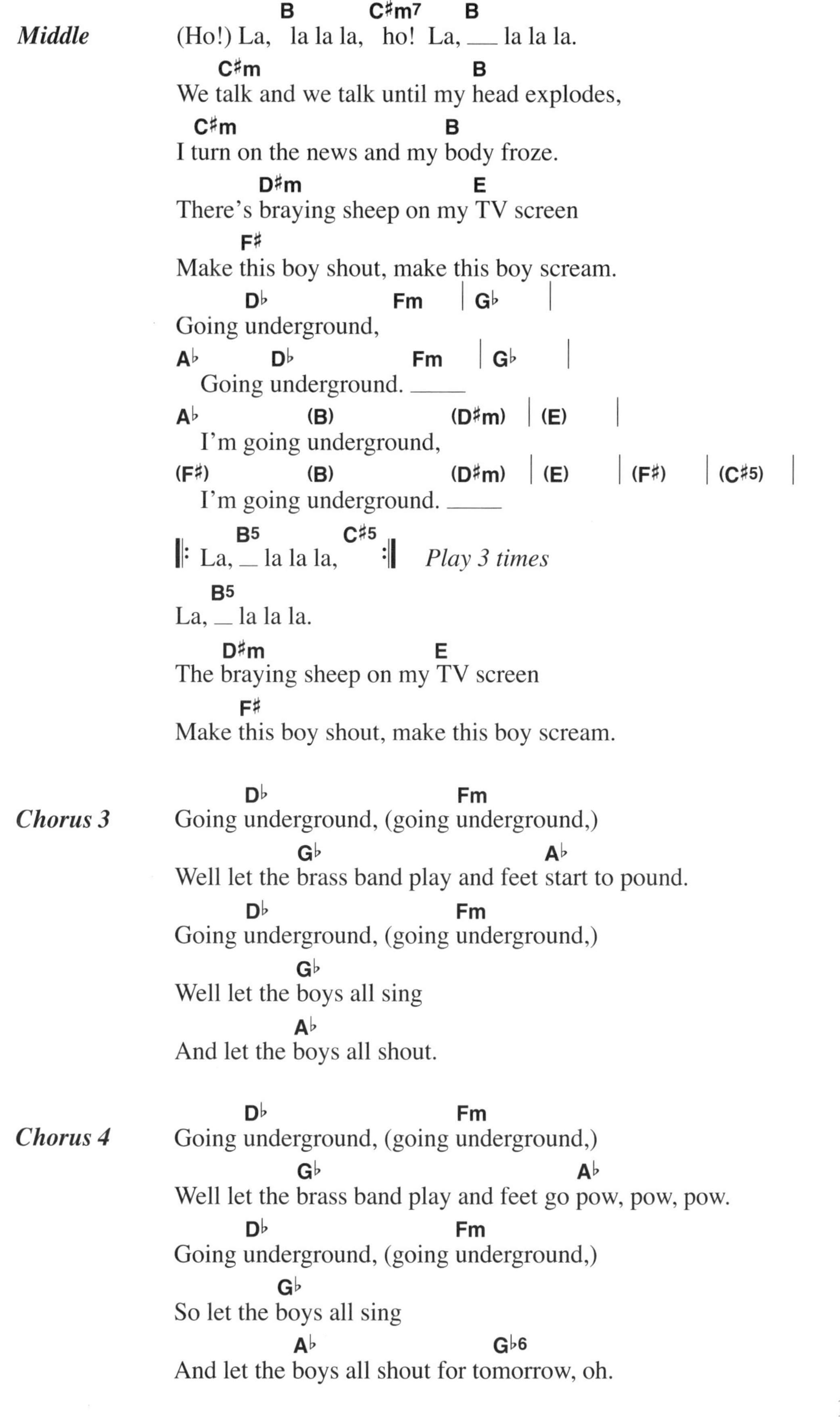

Middle

B C♯m7 B
(Ho!) La, la la la, ho! La, __ la la la.

C♯m B
We talk and we talk until my head explodes,

C♯m B
I turn on the news and my body froze.

D♯m E
There's braying sheep on my TV screen

F♯
Make this boy shout, make this boy scream.

D♭ Fm | G♭ |
Going underground,

A♭ D♭ Fm | G♭ |
Going underground. ____

A♭ (B) (D♯m) | (E) |
I'm going underground,

(F♯) (B) (D♯m) | (E) | (F♯) | (C♯5) |
I'm going underground. ____

B5 C♯5
‖: La, _ la la la, :‖ *Play 3 times*

B5
La, _ la la la.

D♯m E
The braying sheep on my TV screen

F♯
Make this boy shout, make this boy scream.

Chorus 3

D♭ Fm
Going underground, (going underground,)

G♭ A♭
Well let the brass band play and feet start to pound.

D♭ Fm
Going underground, (going underground,)

G♭
Well let the boys all sing

A♭
And let the boys all shout.

Chorus 4

D♭ Fm
Going underground, (going underground,)

G♭ A♭
Well let the brass band play and feet go pow, pow, pow.

D♭ Fm
Going underground, (going underground,)

G♭
So let the boys all sing

A♭ G♭6
And let the boys all shout for tomorrow, oh.

Brass In Pocket

Words & Music by
Chrissie Hynde & James Honeyman-Scott

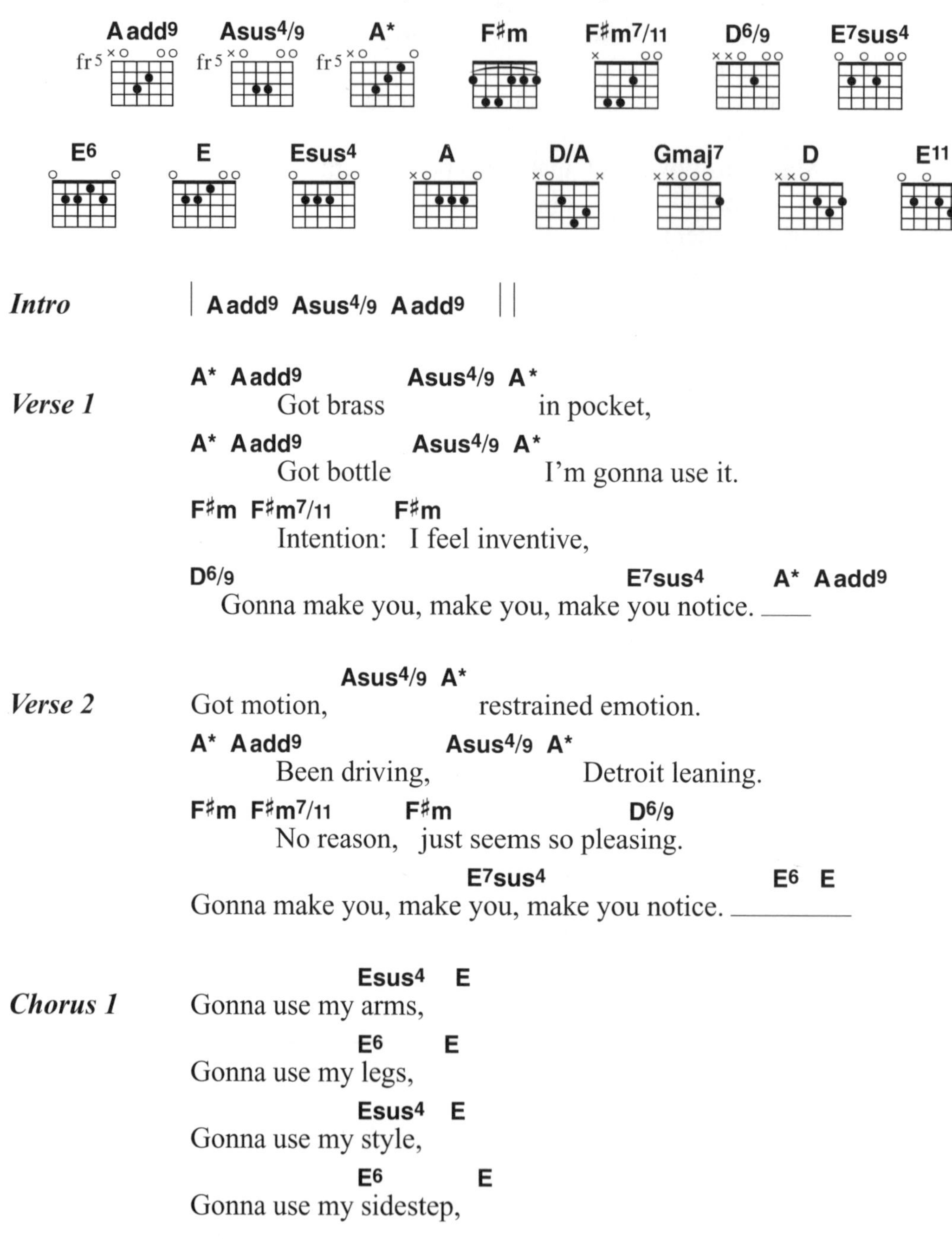

Intro | Aadd9 Asus4/9 Aadd9 ||

Verse 1

A* Aadd9 Asus4/9 A*
Got brass in pocket,
A* Aadd9 Asus4/9 A*
Got bottle I'm gonna use it.
F♯m F♯m7/11 F♯m
Intention: I feel inventive,
D6/9 E7sus4 A* Aadd9
Gonna make you, make you, make you notice. ___

Verse 2

Asus4/9 A*
Got motion, restrained emotion.
A* Aadd9 Asus4/9 A*
Been driving, Detroit leaning.
F♯m F♯m7/11 F♯m D6/9
No reason, just seems so pleasing.
E7sus4 E6 E
Gonna make you, make you, make you notice. ______

Chorus 1

Esus4 E
Gonna use my arms,
E6 E
Gonna use my legs,
Esus4 E
Gonna use my style,
E6 E
Gonna use my sidestep,

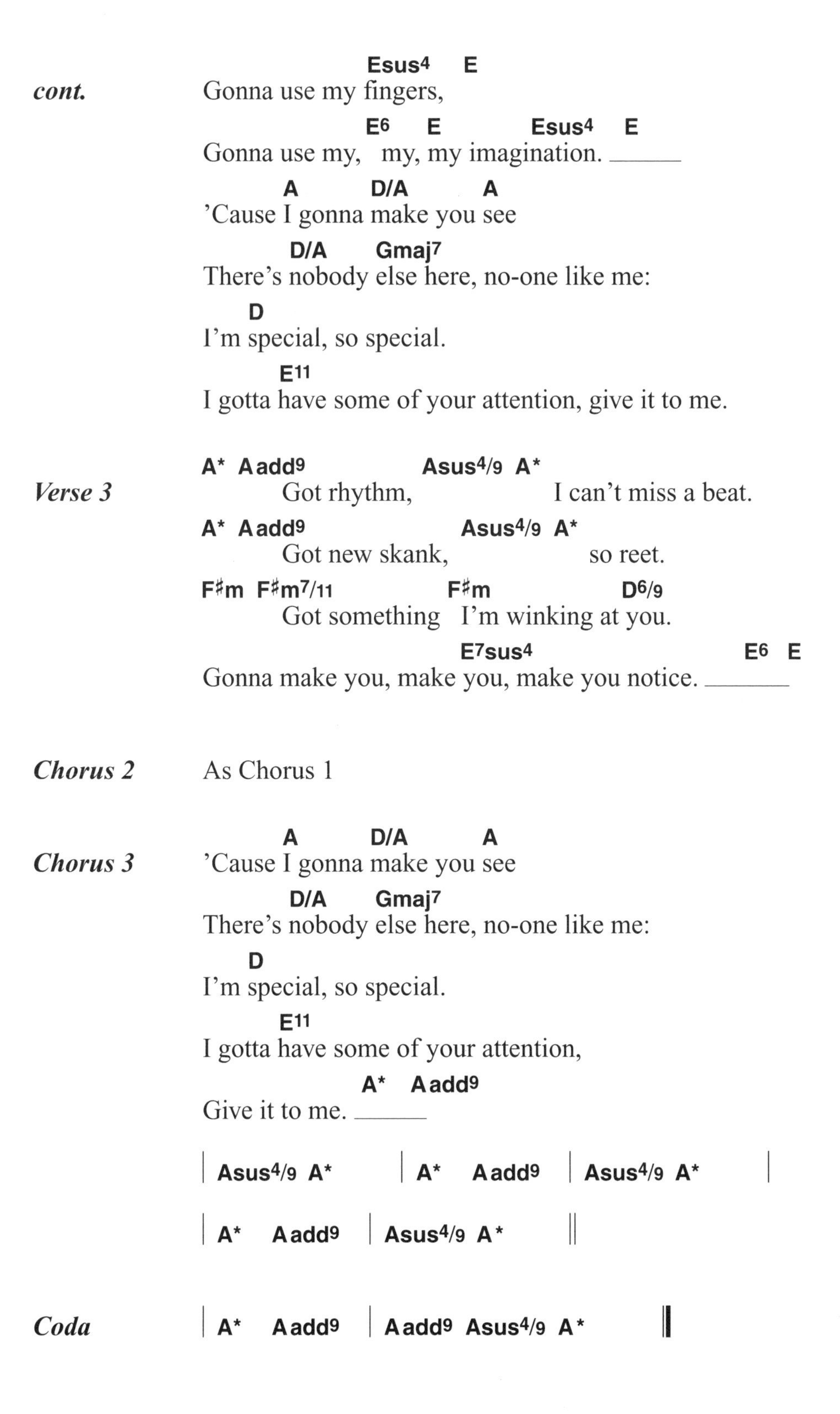

cont.

Esus4 E
Gonna use my fingers,
E6 E Esus4 E
Gonna use my, my, my imagination. ___
A D/A A
'Cause I gonna make you see
D/A Gmaj7
There's nobody else here, no-one like me:
D
I'm special, so special.
E11
I gotta have some of your attention, give it to me.

Verse 3

A* Aadd9 Asus4/9 A*
Got rhythm, I can't miss a beat.
A* Aadd9 Asus4/9 A*
Got new skank, so reet.
F♯m F♯m7/11 F♯m D6/9
Got something I'm winking at you.
E7sus4 E6 E
Gonna make you, make you, make you notice. ___

Chorus 2

As Chorus 1

Chorus 3

A D/A A
'Cause I gonna make you see
D/A Gmaj7
There's nobody else here, no-one like me:
D
I'm special, so special.
E11
I gotta have some of your attention,
A* Aadd9
Give it to me. ___

| Asus4/9 A* | A* Aadd9 | Asus4/9 A* |

| A* Aadd9 | Asus4/9 A* ||

Coda

| A* Aadd9 | Aadd9 Asus4/9 A* ||

Lust For Life

Words & Music by
David Bowie & Iggy Pop

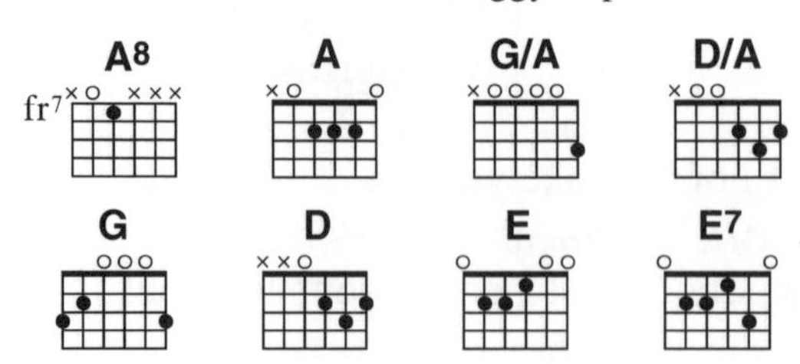

Drum intro

Intro | N.C. | N.C. | N.C. | N.C. |

| A8 | A8 | A8 | A8 | A8 | A8 | A8 | A8 |

‖: A | A G/A D/A :‖ *x4* ‖: E7 :‖ *x8*

‖: A | A G/A D/A :‖ *x4* ‖: E7 :‖ *x8*

| G | G | G | G | D | D | D | D |

| E | E | E | E ‖: A | A G/A D/A :‖ *x2*

Verse 1

```
A                   G/A  D/A  A
Here comes Johnny   Yen    again
          E7
With the liquor and drugs,

And the flesh machine,

He's gonna do another striptease.
A                       G/A  D/A  A           G/A  D/A
Hey man where'd you get   that     lotion?
A                  G/A   D/A  A
I been hurting since I         bought the gimmick
        E7
About something called love,

Yeah something called love

Well that's like hypnotizing chickens.
```

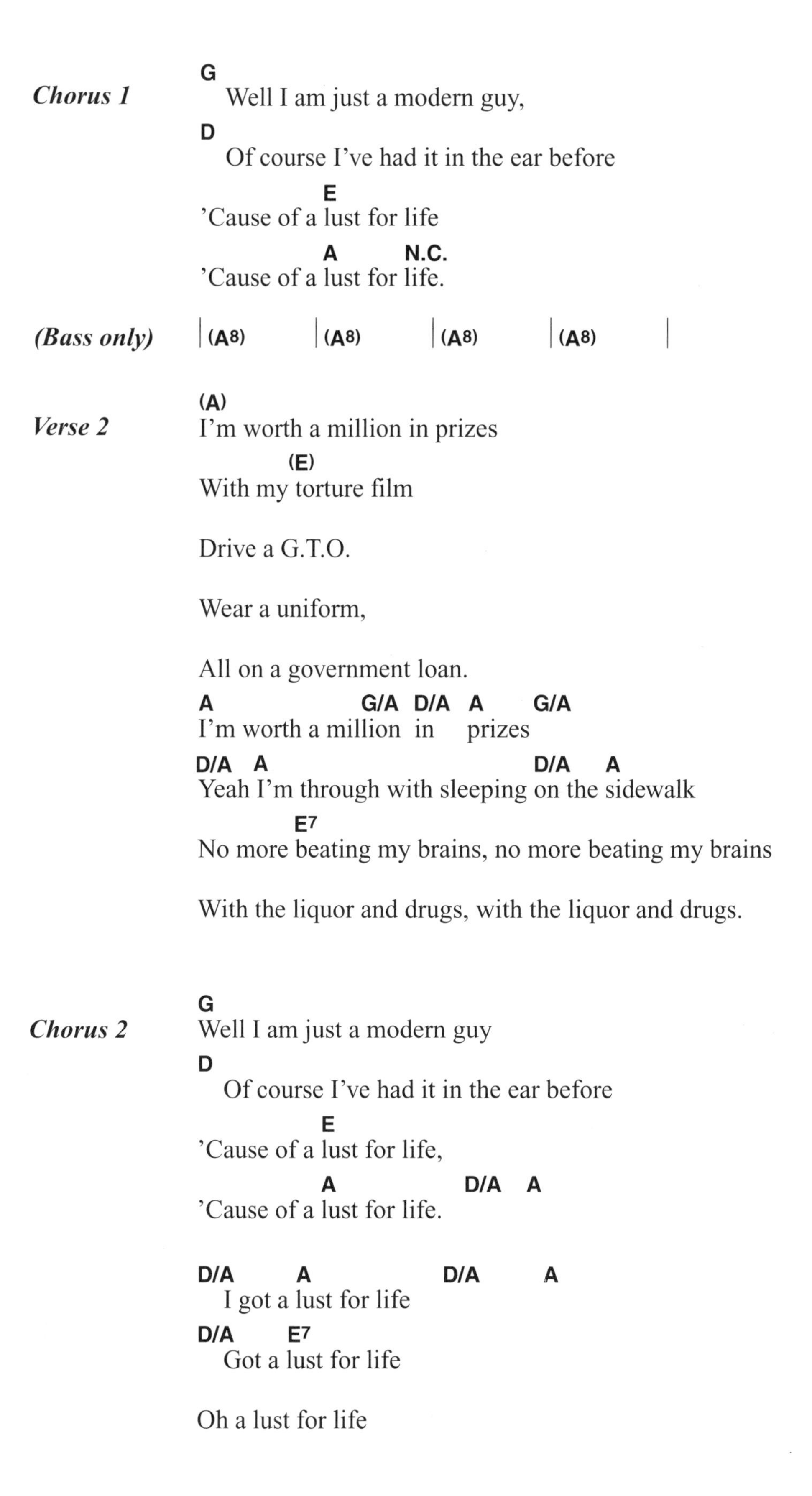

Chorus 1

G
Well I am just a modern guy,
D
Of course I've had it in the ear before
E
'Cause of a lust for life
A N.C.
'Cause of a lust for life.

(Bass only) | (A8) | (A8) | (A8) | (A8) |

Verse 2

(A)
I'm worth a million in prizes
(E)
With my torture film

Drive a G.T.O.

Wear a uniform,

All on a government loan.
A G/A D/A A G/A
I'm worth a million in prizes
D/A A D/A A
Yeah I'm through with sleeping on the sidewalk
E7
No more beating my brains, no more beating my brains

With the liquor and drugs, with the liquor and drugs.

Chorus 2

G
Well I am just a modern guy
D
Of course I've had it in the ear before
E
'Cause of a lust for life,
A D/A A
'Cause of a lust for life.

D/A A D/A A
I got a lust for life
D/A E7
Got a lust for life

Oh a lust for life

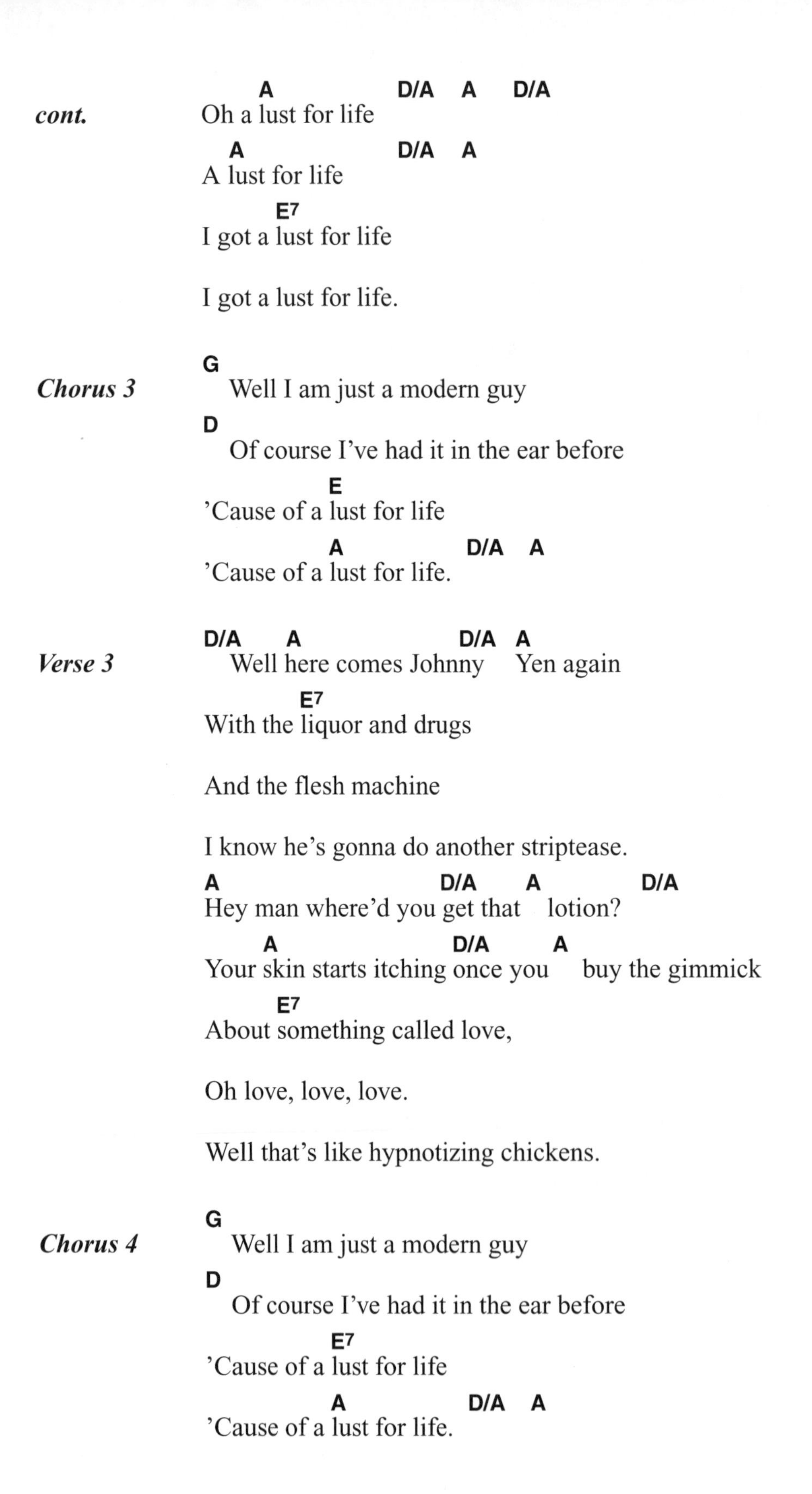

cont.

A D/A A D/A
Oh a lust for life

A D/A A
A lust for life

E7
I got a lust for life

I got a lust for life.

Chorus 3

G
Well I am just a modern guy

D
Of course I've had it in the ear before

E
'Cause of a lust for life

A D/A A
'Cause of a lust for life.

Verse 3

D/A A D/A A
Well here comes Johnny Yen again

E7
With the liquor and drugs

And the flesh machine

I know he's gonna do another striptease.

A D/A A D/A
Hey man where'd you get that lotion?

A D/A A
Your skin starts itching once you buy the gimmick

E7
About something called love,

Oh love, love, love.

Well that's like hypnotizing chickens.

Chorus 4

G
Well I am just a modern guy

D
Of course I've had it in the ear before

E7
'Cause of a lust for life

A D/A A
'Cause of a lust for life.

cont.

```
D/A       A
   Got a lust for life
D/A         A
   Yeah a lust for life,
         E7
I got a lust for life,

I got a lust for life,

I got a lust for life,

I got a lust for life,
          A               D/A
𝄆 I got a lust for life.        𝄇 Repeat to fade
```

Perfect Day

Words & Music by
Lou Reed

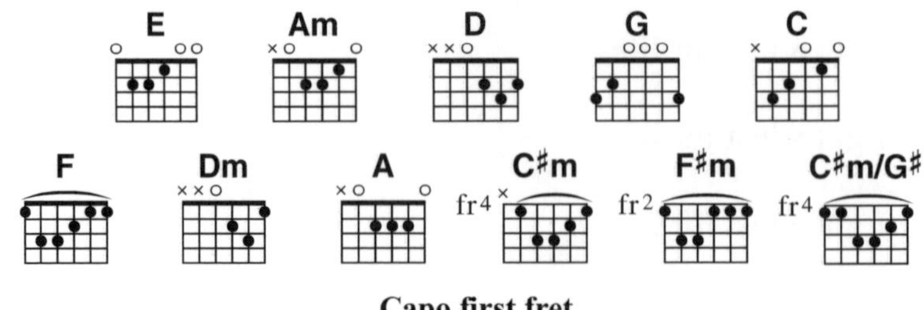

Capo first fret

Intro

```
| E  Am | E  Am ||
```

Verse 1

```
Am      D
  Just a perfect day,
G                C
  Drink sangria in the park,
F                   Dm
  And then later,     when it gets dark,
      E
We go home.
Am      D
  Just a perfect day,
G                C
  Feed animals in the zoo,
F              Dm
  Then later,      a movie too,
         E
And then home.
```

Chorus 1

```
    A        D
Oh, it's such a perfect day,
C♯m                   D
I'm glad I spent it with you.
A           E
  Oh, such a perfect day,
          F♯m     E       D
You just keep me hanging on,
          F♯m     E       D    | D    |
You just keep me hanging on.
```

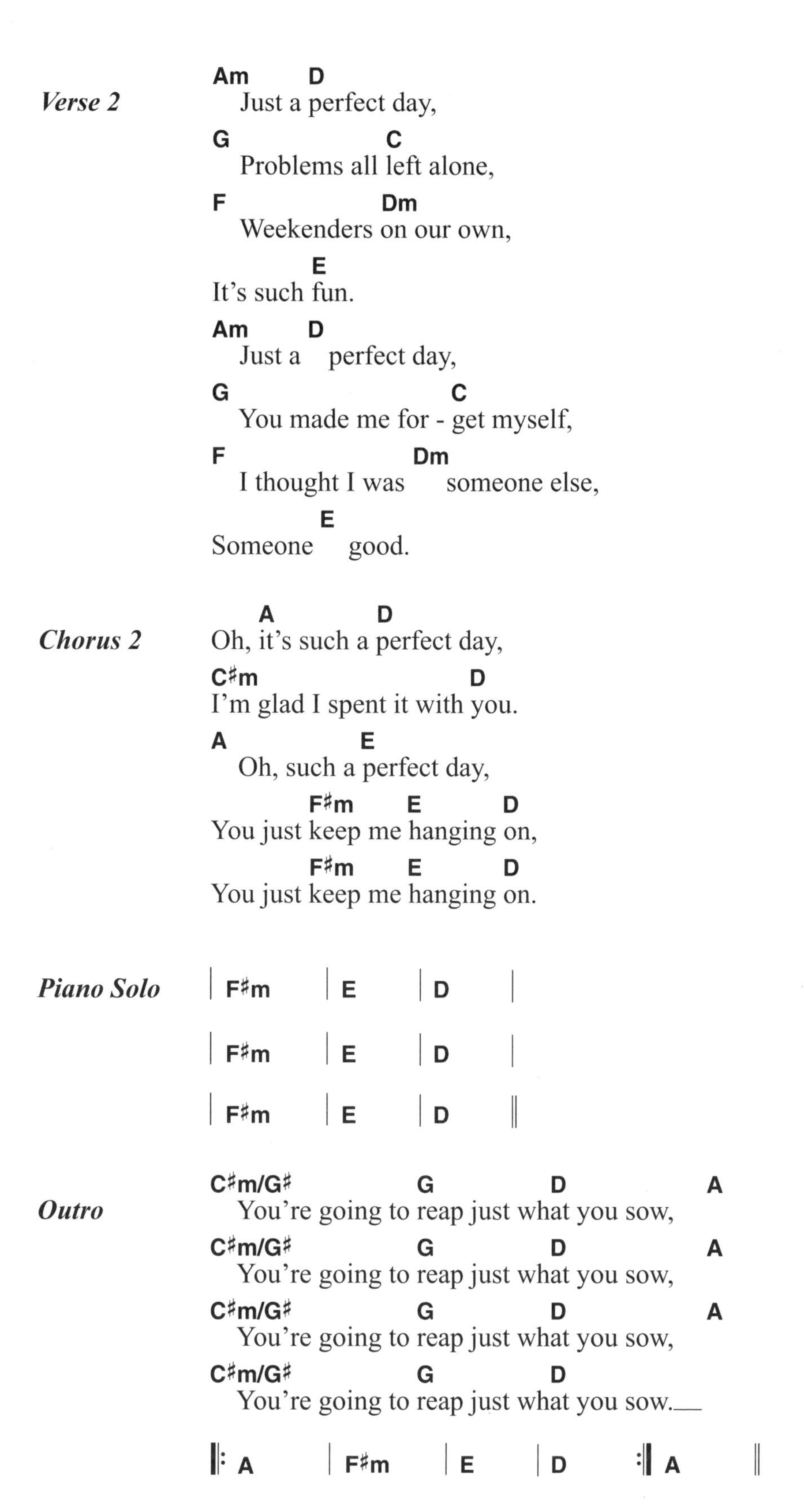
Verse 2
Am D
Just a perfect day,
G C
Problems all left alone,
F Dm
Weekenders on our own,
E
It's such fun.
Am D
Just a perfect day,
G C
You made me for - get myself,
F Dm
I thought I was someone else,
E
Someone good.
Chorus 2
A D
Oh, it's such a perfect day,
C♯m D
I'm glad I spent it with you.
A E
Oh, such a perfect day,
F♯m E D
You just keep me hanging on,
F♯m E D
You just keep me hanging on.
Piano Solo
F♯m	E	D
F♯m	E	D
F♯m	E	D	
Outro
C♯m/G♯ G D A
You're going to reap just what you sow,
C♯m/G♯ G D A
You're going to reap just what you sow,
C♯m/G♯ G D A
You're going to reap just what you sow,
C♯m/G♯ G D
You're going to reap just what you sow.
: A	F♯m	E	D :| A	

Telegram Sam

Words & Music by
Marc Bolan

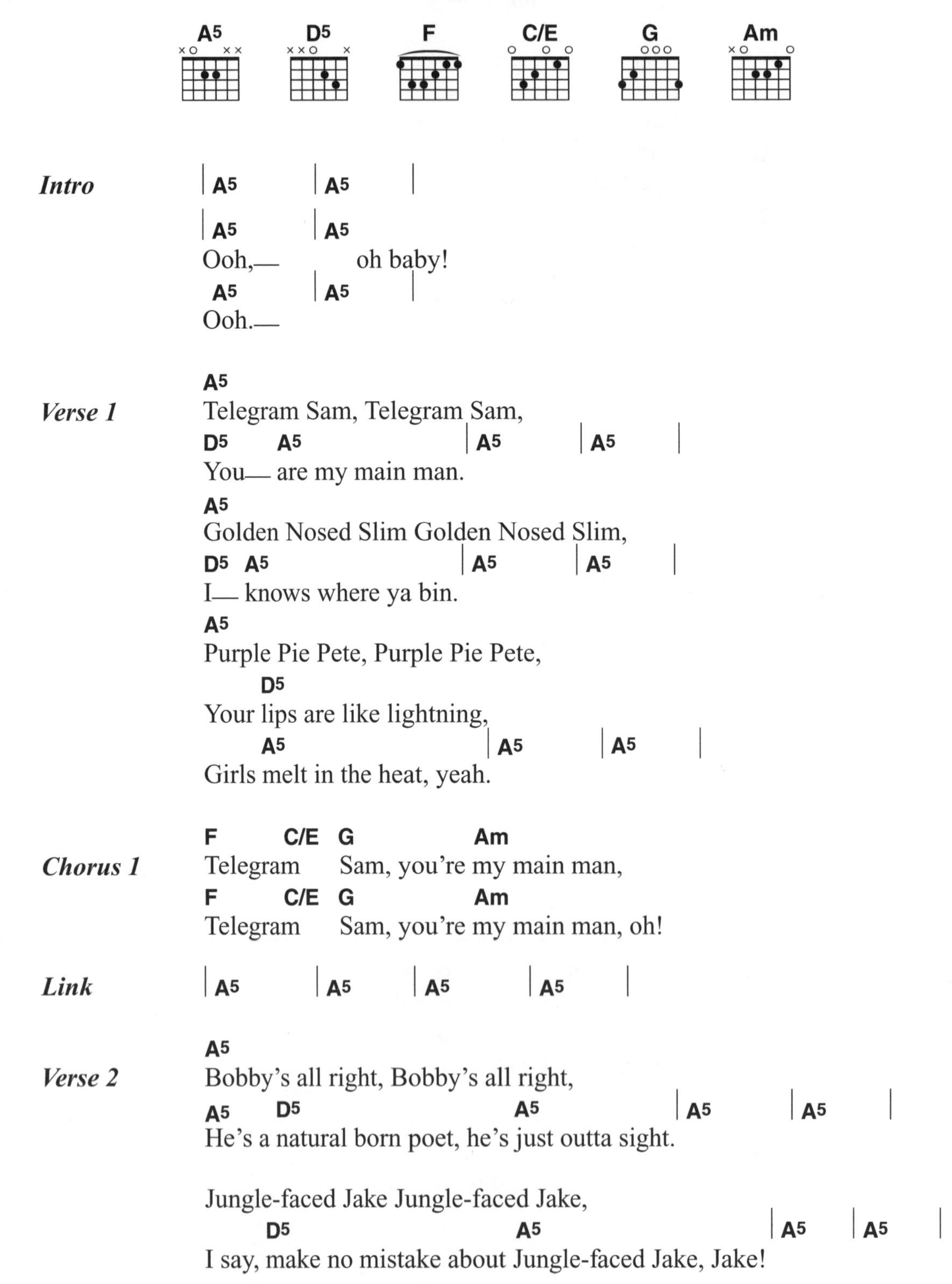

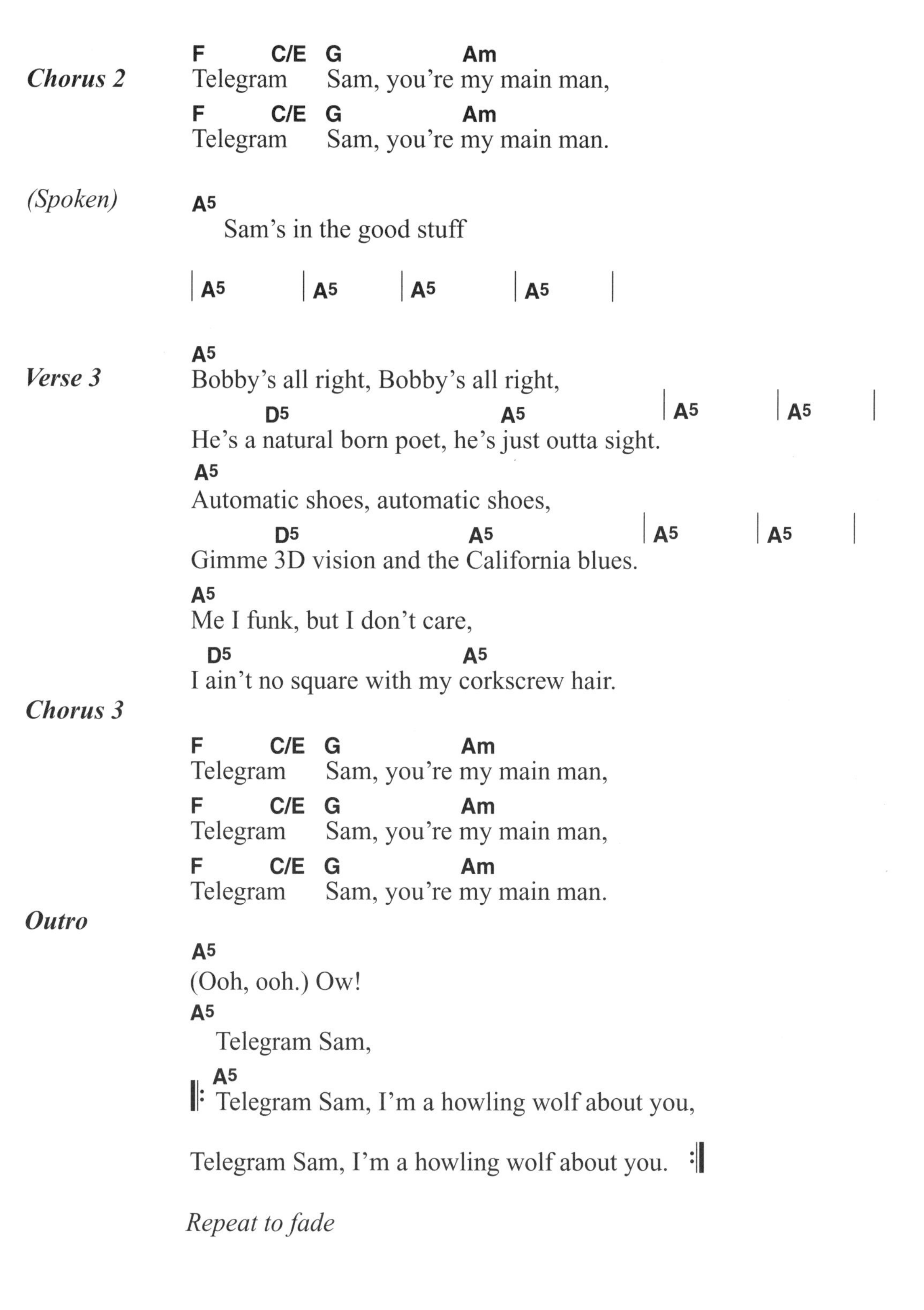
Chorus 2
F C/E G Am
Telegram Sam, you're my main man,
F C/E G Am
Telegram Sam, you're my main man.
(Spoken)
A5
Sam's in the good stuff
| A5 | A5 | A5 | A5 |
Verse 3
A5
Bobby's all right, Bobby's all right,
D5 A5 | A5 | A5 |
He's a natural born poet, he's just outta sight.
A5
Automatic shoes, automatic shoes,
D5 A5 | A5 | A5 |
Gimme 3D vision and the California blues.
A5
Me I funk, but I don't care,
D5 A5
I ain't no square with my corkscrew hair.
Chorus 3
F C/E G Am
Telegram Sam, you're my main man,
F C/E G Am
Telegram Sam, you're my main man,
F C/E G Am
Telegram Sam, you're my main man.
Outro
A5
(Ooh, ooh.) Ow!
A5
Telegram Sam,
A5
Telegram Sam, I'm a howling wolf about you,
Telegram Sam, I'm a howling wolf about you.
Repeat to fade

Should I Stay Or Should I Go

Words & Music by
Joe Strummer & Mick Jones

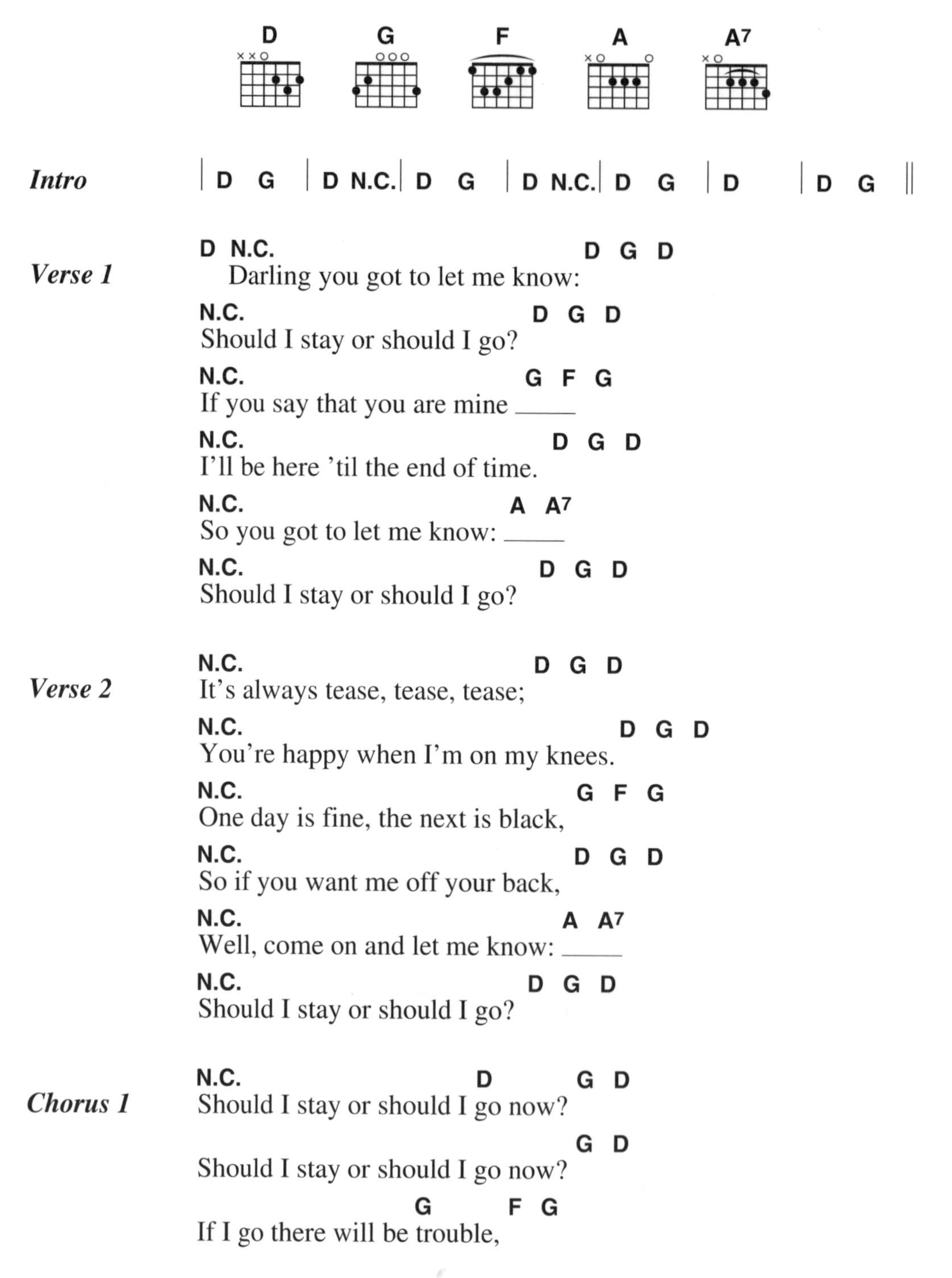

Intro | D G | D N.C. | D G | D N.C. | D G | D | D G ||

Verse 1

D N.C. D G D
Darling you got to let me know:
N.C. D G D
Should I stay or should I go?
N.C. G F G
If you say that you are mine _____
N.C. D G D
I'll be here 'til the end of time.
N.C. A A7
So you got to let me know: _____
N.C. D G D
Should I stay or should I go?

Verse 2

N.C. D G D
It's always tease, tease, tease;
N.C. D G D
You're happy when I'm on my knees.
N.C. G F G
One day is fine, the next is black,
N.C. D G D
So if you want me off your back,
N.C. A A7
Well, come on and let me know: _____
N.C. D G D
Should I stay or should I go?

Chorus 1

N.C. D G D
Should I stay or should I go now?
G D
Should I stay or should I go now?
G F G
If I go there will be trouble,

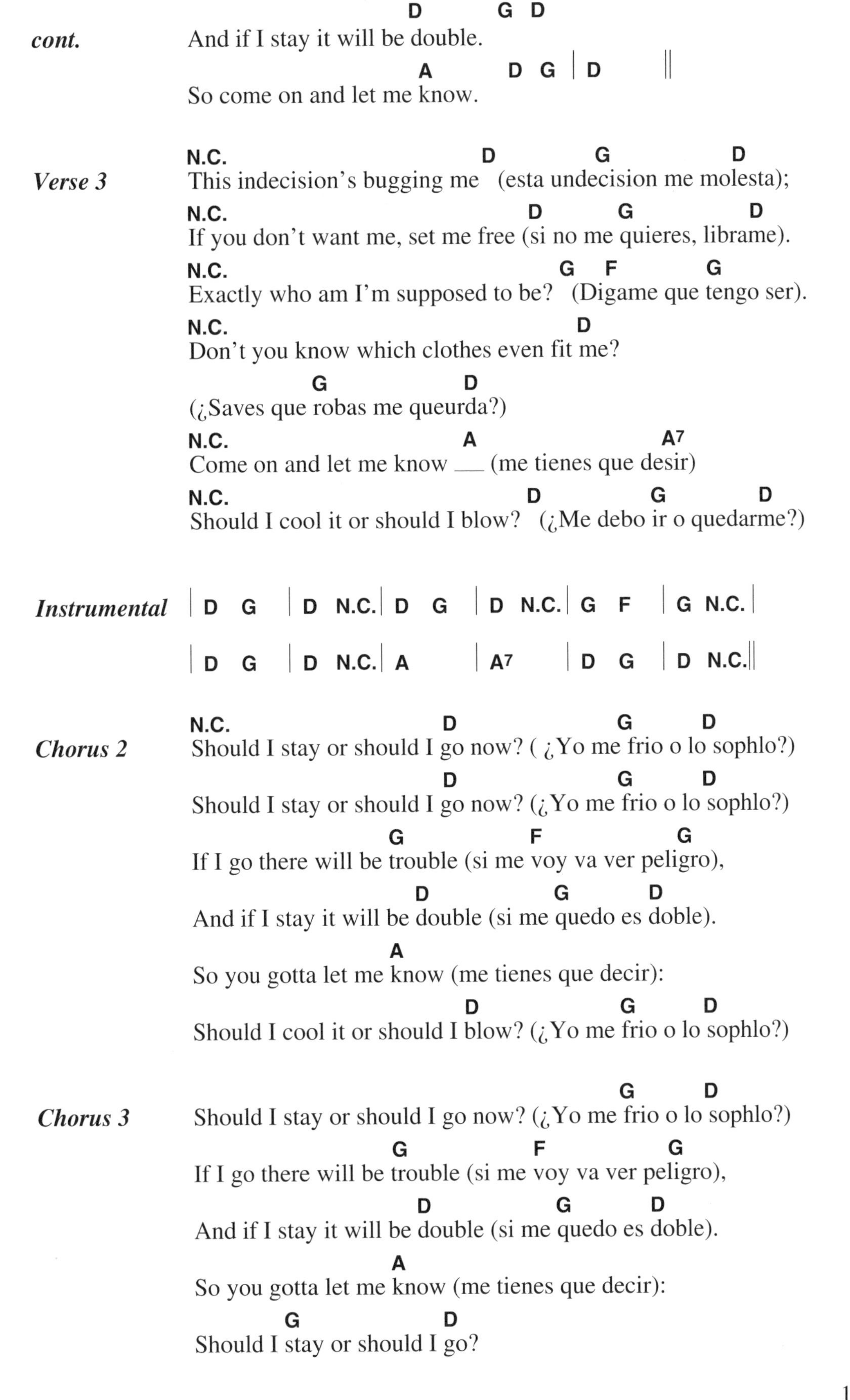

cont.

D G D
And if I stay it will be double.
A D G | D ||
So come on and let me know.

Verse 3

N.C. D G D
This indecision's bugging me (esta undecision me molesta);
N.C. D G D
If you don't want me, set me free (si no me quieres, librame).
N.C. G F G
Exactly who am I'm supposed to be? (Digame que tengo ser).
N.C. D
Don't you know which clothes even fit me?
G D
(¿Saves que robas me queurda?)
N.C. A A7
Come on and let me know ___ (me tienes que desir)
N.C. D G D
Should I cool it or should I blow? (¿Me debo ir o quedarme?)

Instrumental

| D G | D N.C. | D G | D N.C. | G F | G N.C. |
| D G | D N.C. | A | A7 | D G | D N.C. ||

Chorus 2

N.C. D G D
Should I stay or should I go now? (¿Yo me frio o lo sophlo?)
D G D
Should I stay or should I go now? (¿Yo me frio o lo sophlo?)
G F G
If I go there will be trouble (si me voy va ver peligro),
D G D
And if I stay it will be double (si me quedo es doble).
A
So you gotta let me know (me tienes que decir):
D G D
Should I cool it or should I blow? (¿Yo me frio o lo sophlo?)

Chorus 3

G D
Should I stay or should I go now? (¿Yo me frio o lo sophlo?)
G F G
If I go there will be trouble (si me voy va ver peligro),
D G D
And if I stay it will be double (si me quedo es doble).
A
So you gotta let me know (me tienes que decir):
G D
Should I stay or should I go?

True Faith

Words & Music by
Peter Hook, Stephen Hague, Bernard Sumner, Gillian Gilbert & Stephen Morris

Dm F C G B♭
Am A Dmadd4 Dm* A7
fr8 fr5 fr5

Drums
4

Intro | 4 ||

Dm	F	C	G
Dm	F	C	G
Dm	F	C	B♭	B♭	

Verse 1

```
Dm                B♭      C
I feel so extra - ordin - ary,
Am                                    C
Something's got a hold on me.
  Dm                B♭    C
I get this feeling I'm in motion,
  Am                C
A sudden sense of liberty.
Dm                  C
I don't care 'cause I'm not there,
     B♭                    Am
And I don't care if I'm here tomorrow,
   C                        B♭
A - gain and again I've taken too much
Am                                 A
Of the things that cost you too much.
```

Chorus 1

```
Dm                             F                 C
   I used to think that the day would never come,
                           G                    Dm
I'd see delight in the shade of the morning sun,
                                F                  C
My morning sun is the drug that brings me near
                             G
To the childhood I lost, replaced by fear.
```

cont.

Dm F C
I used to think that the day would never come,
B♭ | B♭ | B♭ |
That my life would de - pend on the morning sun.__

Verse 2

Dm B♭ C
When I was a very small boy,
Am C
Very small boys talked to me.
Dm B♭ C
Now that we've grown up to - gether
Am C
They're afraid of what they see
Dm C
That's the price that we all pay
B♭ Am
Our valued destiny comes to nothing
C B♭
I can't tell you where we're going
Am A
I guess there's just no way of knowing.

Chorus 2

Dm F C
I used to think that the day would never come,
G Dm
I'd see delight in the shade of the morning sun,
F C
My morning sun is the drug that brings me near
G
To the childhood I lost, replaced by fear.
Dm F C
I used to think that the day would never come,
B♭ | B♭ | B♭ | B♭
That my life would de - pend on the morning sun.__

Instrumental | Dm(add4) | Dm* | Dm(add4) | Dm* |

| Dm(add4) | Dm* | Dm(add4) | A7 ||

| Dm | F | C | G |

| Dm | F | C | G |

| Dm | F | C | B♭ | B♭ ||

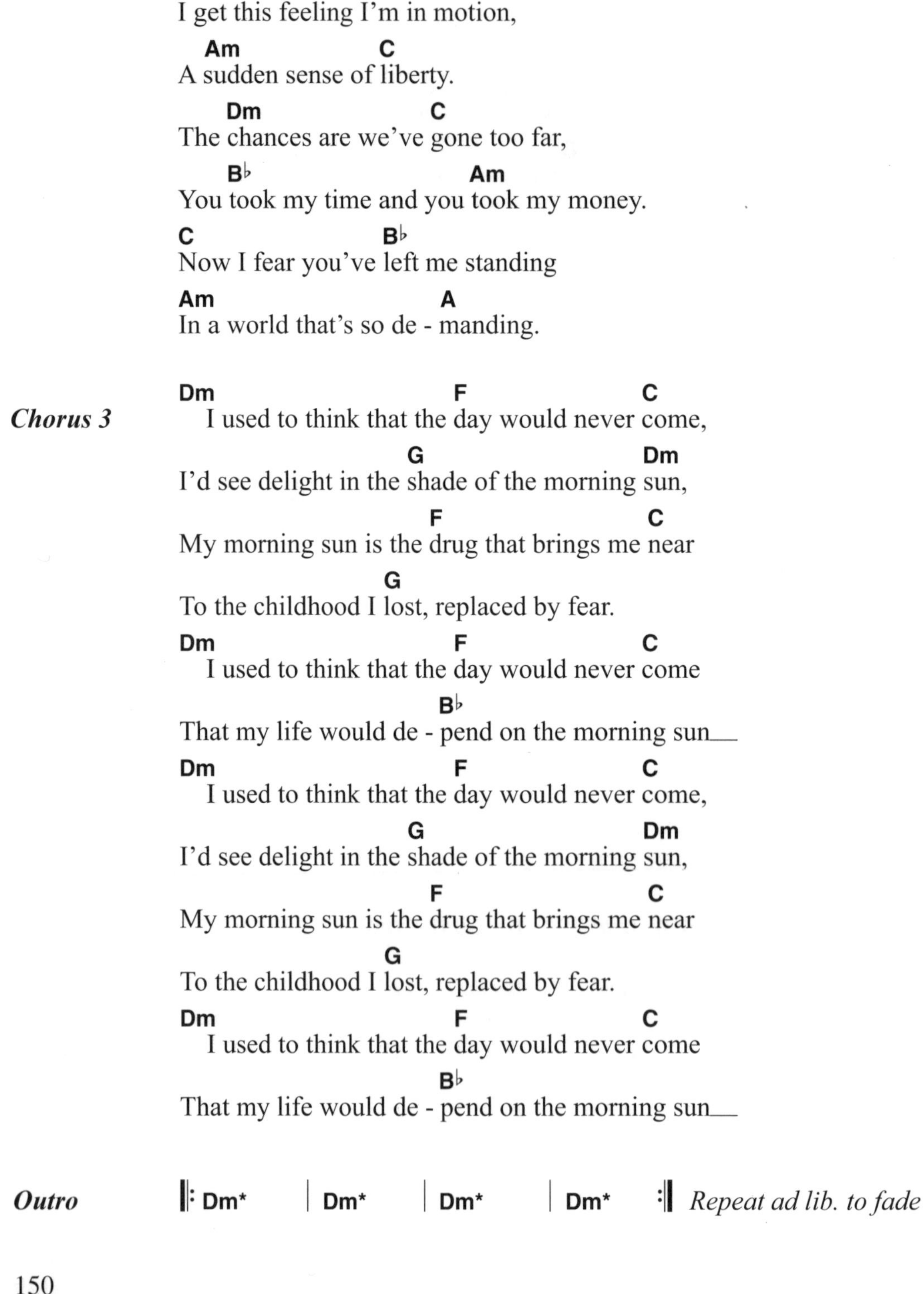
Verse 3
Dm Bb C
I feel so extra - ordin - ary,
Am C
Something's got a hold on me.
Dm Bb C
I get this feeling I'm in motion,
Am C
A sudden sense of liberty.
Dm C
The chances are we've gone too far,
Bb Am
You took my time and you took my money.
C Bb
Now I fear you've left me standing
Am A
In a world that's so de - manding.
Chorus 3
Dm F C
I used to think that the day would never come,
G Dm
I'd see delight in the shade of the morning sun,
F C
My morning sun is the drug that brings me near
G
To the childhood I lost, replaced by fear.
Dm F C
I used to think that the day would never come
Bb
That my life would de - pend on the morning sun__
Dm F C
I used to think that the day would never come,
G Dm
I'd see delight in the shade of the morning sun,
F C
My morning sun is the drug that brings me near
G
To the childhood I lost, replaced by fear.
Dm F C
I used to think that the day would never come
Bb
That my life would de - pend on the morning sun__
Outro
‖: Dm* | Dm* | Dm* | Dm* :‖ Repeat ad lib. to fade

Fools Gold

Words & Music by
John Squire & Ian Brown

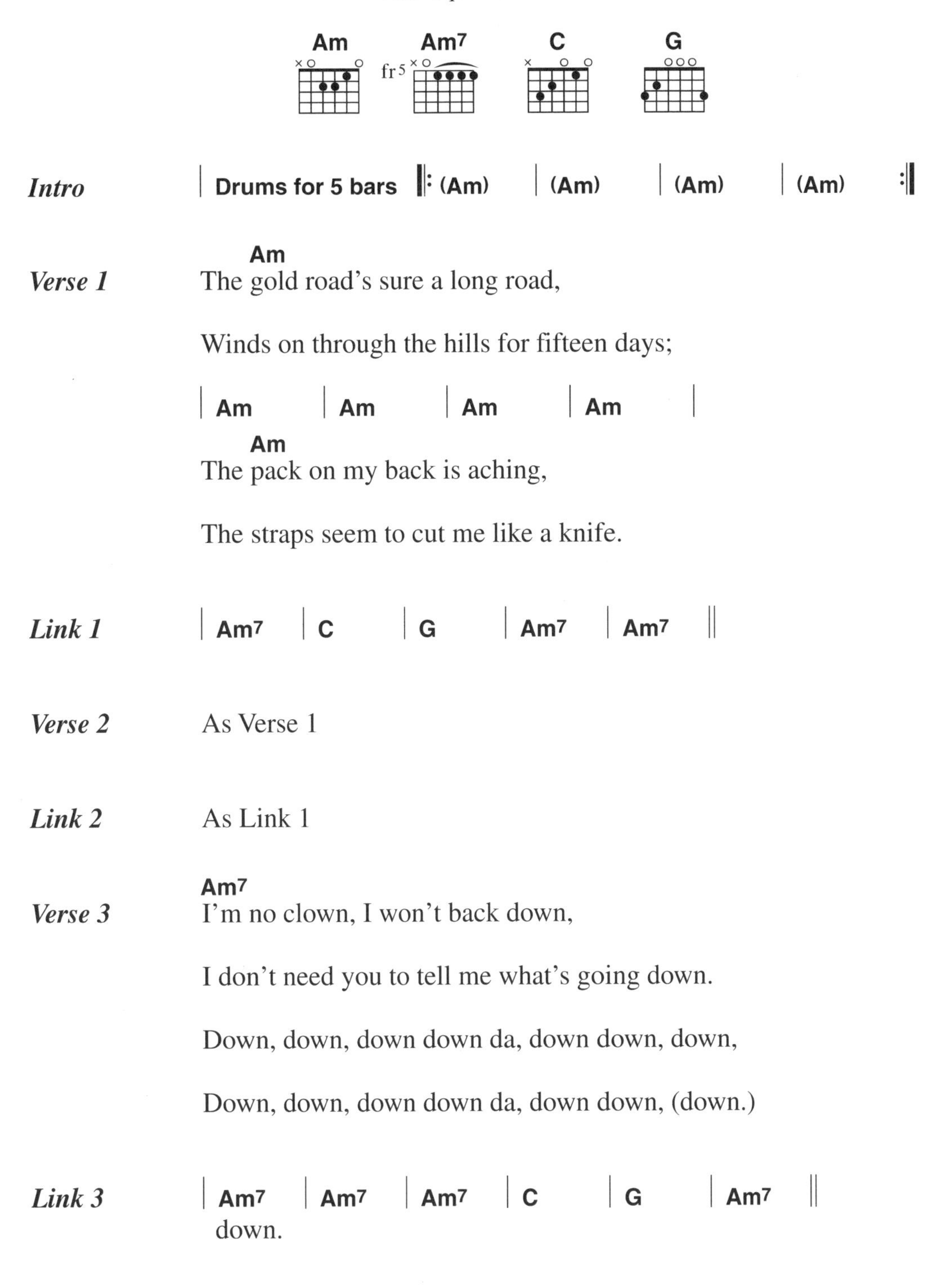

Intro | Drums for 5 bars ||: (Am) | (Am) | (Am) | (Am) :||

Verse 1

Am
The gold road's sure a long road,

Winds on through the hills for fifteen days;

| **Am** | **Am** | **Am** | **Am** |

Am
The pack on my back is aching,

The straps seem to cut me like a knife.

Link 1 | **Am7** | **C** | **G** | **Am7** | **Am7** ||

Verse 2 As Verse 1

Link 2 As Link 1

Verse 3

Am7
I'm no clown, I won't back down,

I don't need you to tell me what's going down.

Down, down, down down da, down down, down,

Down, down, down down da, down down, (down.)

Link 3 | **Am7** | **Am7** | **Am7** | **C** | **G** | **Am7** ||
down.

Chorus 1

```
Am7            C                  G
   I'm standing alone, I'm watching you all,
             Am7
I'm seeing you sinking.
            C                  G
I'm standing alone, you're weighing the gold,
                 Am7
I'm watching you sinking.

Fool's (gold.)
```

Link 4

```
| Am7  | Am7  | Am7    | Am7    ||
  gold.
```

Verse 4

```
      Am7
These boots were made for walking,

The Marquis de Sade never made no boots like these.

| Am7    | Am7    | Am7    | Am7    |
    Am7
Gold's just around the corner,

Breakdown's coming up round the bend.
```

Link 5

```
| Am7    | Am7    | Am7    | Am7    ||
Am7
Sometimes you have to try to get along, dear,

I know the truth and I know what you're thinking.

Down, down, down down da, down down, down.
```

Link 6

```
| Drum break || Am7  | C    | G    | Am7   ||
```

Chorus 2 As Chorus 1

Link 7

```
| Am7  | Am7  | Am7  | Am7          | Am7       | Am7   ||
  gold.                   Fool's __   gold. __
```

Instrumental ‖: Am7 | Am7 | Am7 | Am7 :‖

| Am7 | C | G | Am7 ‖

Chorus 3

```
Am7                C                        G
   I'm standing alone, I'm watching you all,
                Am7
I'm seeing you sinking.
                C                        G
I'm standing alone, you're weighing the gold,
                   Am7
I'm watching you sinking.
```

Fool's (gold.)

Link 8 | Am7 | (Am7) | (Am7) | (Am7) | (Am7) | (Am7) ‖

gold. Fool's __ gold. __

Coda ‖: (Am7) | (Am7) | (Am7) | (Am7) :‖ *Ad lib instrumental to end*

This Charming Man

Words & Music by
Morrissey & Johnny Marr

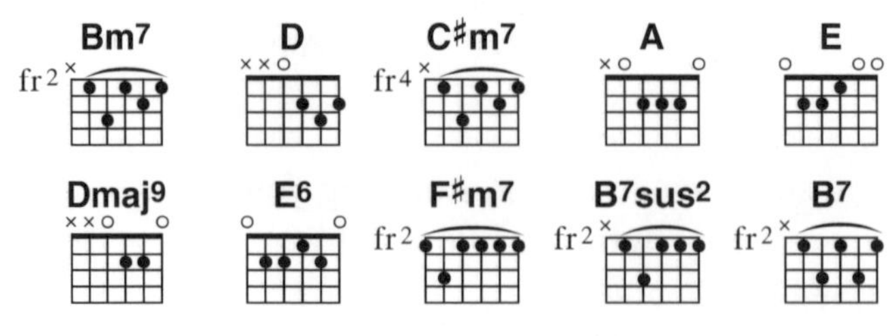

Tune guitar slightly flat

Intro | Bm7 | D | C♯m7 | A ||

Verse 1
N.C. Bm7
Punctured bicycle
D C♯m7 A
On a hillside desolate,
E Bm7 | D | C♯m7
Will nature make a man of me yet?
A
When in this charming car,
E Bm7 D C♯m7
This charm - ing man.
A
Why pamper life's complexity

When the leather runs smooth
E Bm7 D C♯m7
On the passenger seat?______

Pre-chorus 1
A
I would go out tonight
E Bm7 D C♯m7
But I haven't got a stitch to wear,
A
This man said it's gruesome
E Bm7 D C♯m7
That someone so handsome should care.______

Chorus 1

Dmaj9 E6 | F♯m7
Ah! A jumped-up pantry boy
B7sus2 Dmaj9
Who never knew his place,
B7 F♯m7
He said, "Re - turn the ring".
Dmaj9 E6 F♯m7 B7sus2
He knows so much a - bout these things,
Dmaj9 E6 F♯m7
He knows so much a - bout these things.

Pre-chorus 2

N.C. A
I would go out tonight
E Bm7 D C♯m7
But I haven't got a stitch to wear,
A
This man said it's gruesome
E | Bm7 D C♯m7
That someone so handsome should care__
A E Bm7 D C♯m7
La, la-la, la-la, la-la, this charm - ing man__
A E Bm7 D C♯m7
Oh, la-la, la-la, la-la, this charm - ing man__

Chorus 2

Dmaj9 E6 F♯m7
Ah! a jumped-up pantry boy
B7sus2 Dmaj9
Who never knew his place,
B7 F♯m7
He said, "Re - turn the ring".
Dmaj9 E6 F♯m7 B7sus2
He knows so much about these things,
Dmaj9 E6 F♯m7
He knows so much a - bout these things.
Dmaj9 E6 F♯m7 B7sus2 Dmaj9 B7 F♯m7
He knows so much a - bout these things.________

Outro

| Dmaj9 | E6 | F♯m7 | B7sus2 | Dmaj9 | B7 | F♯m7 | F♯m7 ||

A Design For Life

Words by Nicky Wire
Music by James Dean Bradfield, Nicky Wire & Sean Moore

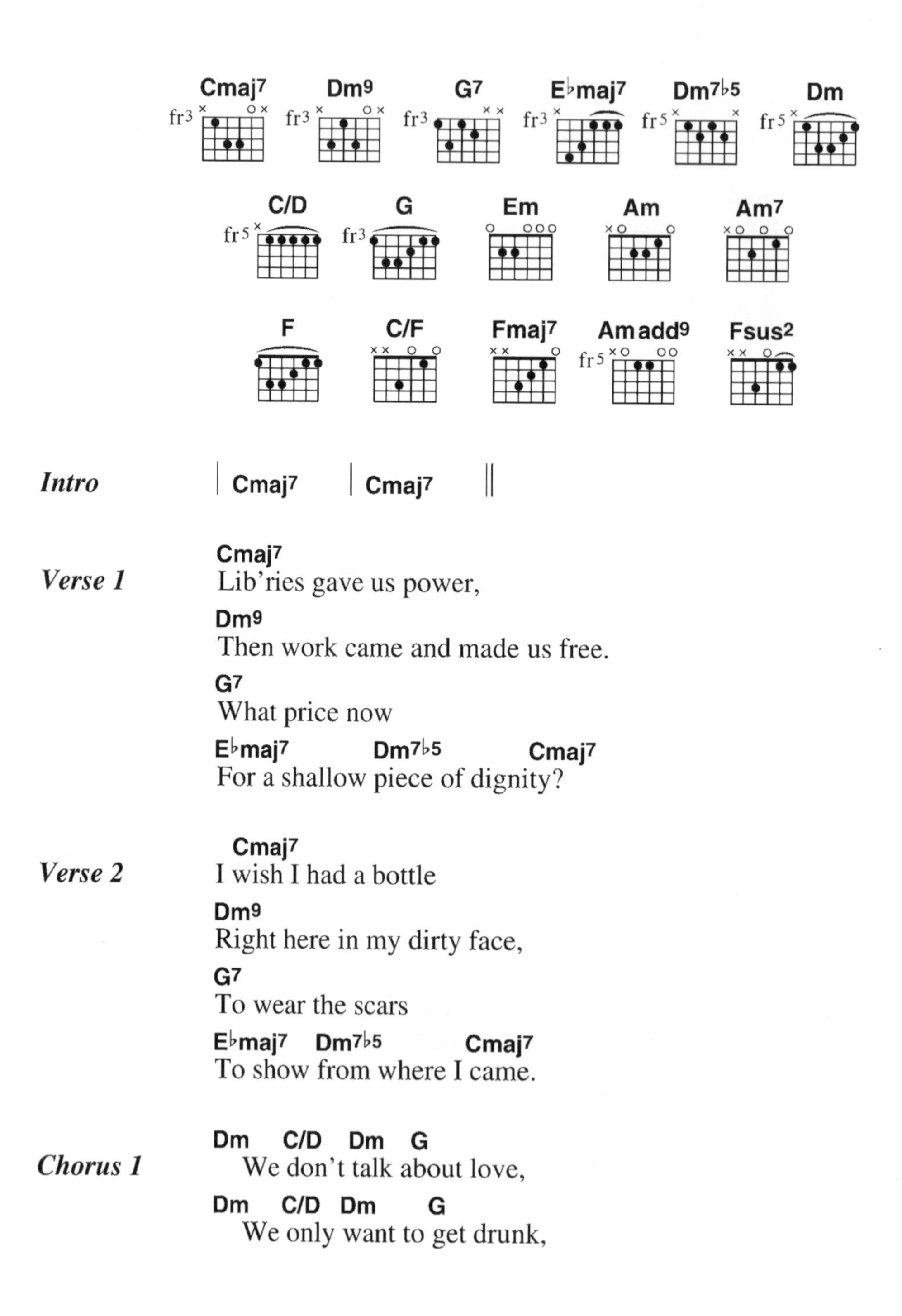

Intro | Cmaj7 | Cmaj7 ||

Verse 1

Cmaj7
Lib'ries gave us power,
Dm9
Then work came and made us free.
G7
What price now
E♭maj7 Dm7♭5 Cmaj7
For a shallow piece of dignity?

Verse 2

Cmaj7
I wish I had a bottle
Dm9
Right here in my dirty face,
G7
To wear the scars
E♭maj7 Dm7♭5 Cmaj7
To show from where I came.

Chorus 1

Dm C/D Dm G
We don't talk about love,
Dm C/D Dm G
We only want to get drunk,

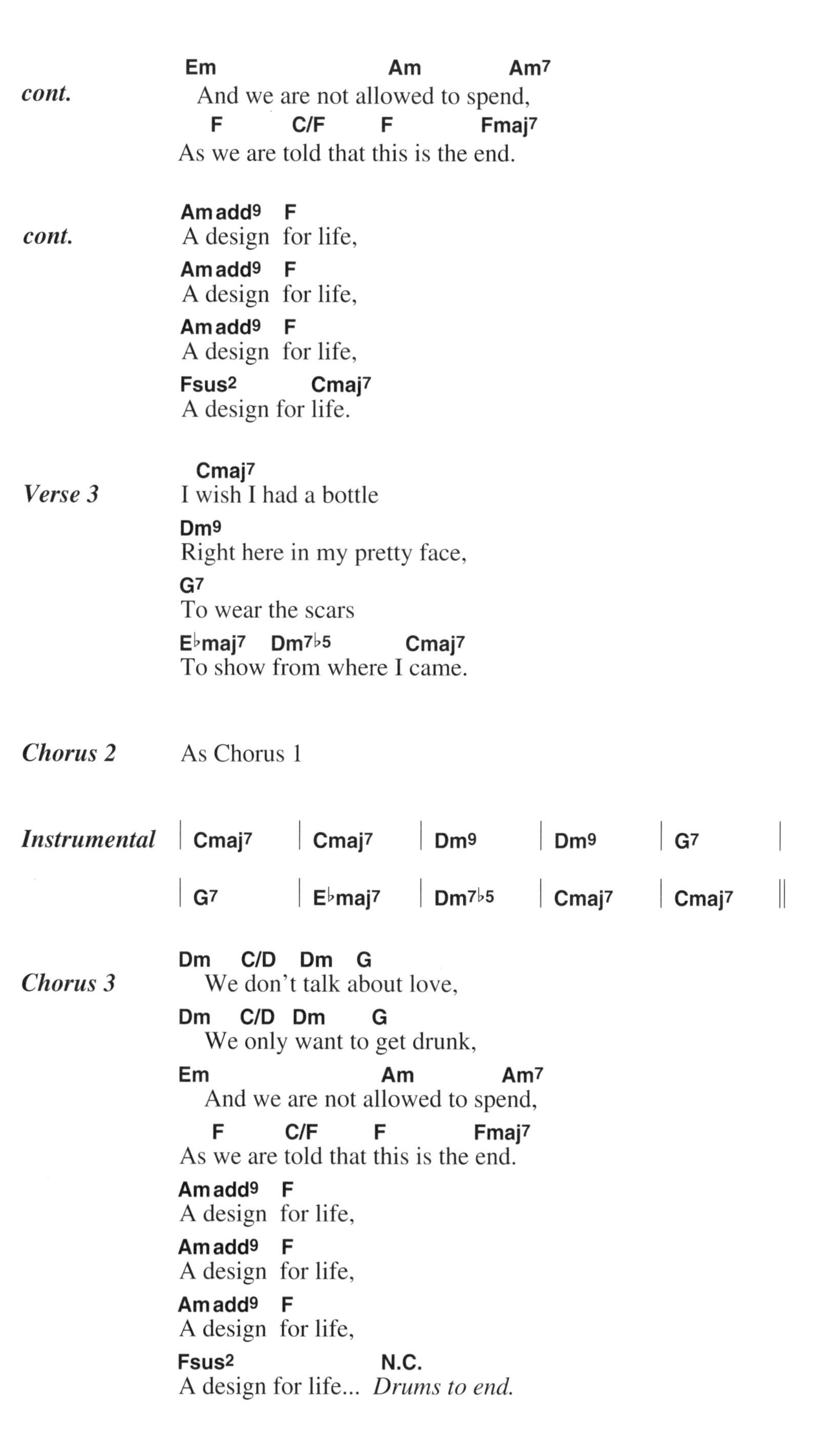

cont.

Em Am Am7
And we are not allowed to spend,
F C/F F Fmaj7
As we are told that this is the end.

cont.

Amadd9 F
A design for life,
Amadd9 F
A design for life,
Amadd9 F
A design for life,
Fsus2 Cmaj7
A design for life.

Verse 3

Cmaj7
I wish I had a bottle
Dm9
Right here in my pretty face,
G7
To wear the scars
E♭maj7 Dm7♭5 Cmaj7
To show from where I came.

Chorus 2

As Chorus 1

Instrumental

| Cmaj7 | Cmaj7 | Dm9 | Dm9 | G7 |
| G7 | E♭maj7 | Dm7♭5 | Cmaj7 | Cmaj7 ||

Chorus 3

Dm C/D Dm G
We don't talk about love,
Dm C/D Dm G
We only want to get drunk,
Em Am Am7
And we are not allowed to spend,
F C/F F Fmaj7
As we are told that this is the end.
Amadd9 F
A design for life,
Amadd9 F
A design for life,
Amadd9 F
A design for life,
Fsus2 N.C.
A design for life... *Drums to end.*

The World's Greatest

Words & Music by
R. Kelly

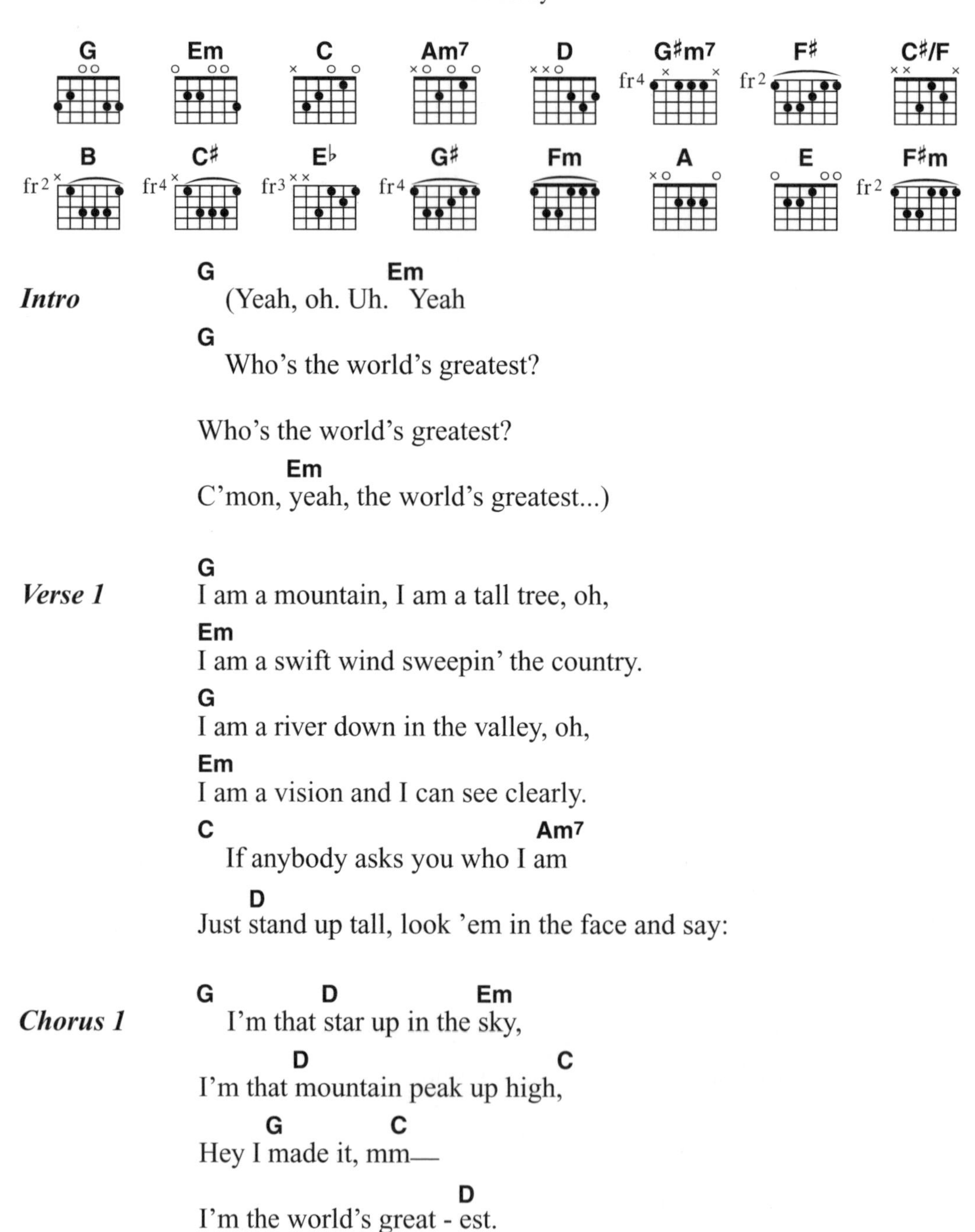

Intro

G (Yeah, oh. Uh. Em Yeah
G Who's the world's greatest?
Who's the world's greatest?
C'mon, Em yeah, the world's greatest...)

Verse 1

G I am a mountain, I am a tall tree, oh,
Em I am a swift wind sweepin' the country.
G I am a river down in the valley, oh,
Em I am a vision and I can see clearly.
C If anybody asks you who I Am7 am
Just D stand up tall, look 'em in the face and say:

Chorus 1

G I'm that D star up in the Em sky,
I'm that D mountain peak up C high,
Hey I G made it, C mm—
I'm the world's great - D est.

```
              G               D           Em
cont.           And I'm that little bit of hope,

                      D                         C
              When my back's against the ropes,

                    G          C
              I can feel it,  mm—

                                        D
              I'm the world's great - est.


              G
Break           (Huh, the world's greatest,

                                     Em
              The world's greatest,    forever.)


              G
Verse 2       I am a giant, I am an eagle, oh,

              Em
              I am a lion, down in the jungle.

              G
              I am a marchin' band, I am the people, oh

              Em
              I am a helpin' hand, I am a hero.

              C                                   Am7
              If anybody asks you who I am

                 D
              Just stand up tall,

              Look 'em in the face and say,—


              G          D               Em
Chorus 2        I'm that star up in the sky,

                        D                      C
              I'm that mountain peak up high,

                      G              C
              Hey I made it, mm—

                                        D
              I'm the world's great - est.

              G               D           Em
                And I'm that little bit of hope,

                      D                         C
              When my back's against the ropes,

                    G            C
              I can feel it, mm—

                                        D
              I'm the world's great - est.——
```

Bridge

G♯m7 F♯ C♯/F
In the ring of life, I'll rein love, (I will rein)

B C♯ F♯
And the world will notice a king (oh yeah,—)

G♯m7 F♯ C♯/F
When there is darkness I'll shine a light (shine a light,—)

B C♯ F♯ E♭
And you'll use the suc - cess you'll find in me (me,—)

Chorus 3

G♯ E♭ Fm
I'm that star up in the sky

E♭ C♯
I'm that mountain peak up high

G♯ C♯ E♭
Hey, I made it I'm the worlds great - est

G♯ E♭ Fm E♭ C♯
I'm that little bit of hope when my back's against the ropes

G♯ C♯ E♭
I can feel it I'm the world's great - est.

A E F♯m
Oh, I'm that star up in the sky

E D
I'm that mountain peak up high

A D E
Hey I made it I'm the world's great - est

A E F♯m E D
I'm that little bit of hope when my back's against the ropes oh,

A D E
I can feel it, I'm the worlds great - est

A E F♯m E
I saw the light, at the end of a tunnel

D A D E
Believe in the pot of gold at the end of the rainbow

A E F♯m E
And faith was right there to pull me through, yeah.

D A D E
Used to be locked doors, now I can just walk on through

A E F♯m E
It's the great - est, can you feel it?

D A D E
Say the great - est, can you feel it?

A E F♯m E
I saw the light at the end of a tunnel

D A D E
Believe in the pot of gold at the end of the rainbow

A E F♯m E
And faith was right there to pull me through, yeah... *Fade*

3 4 5 6 7 8 9
12/07(64465)